BIRDS

THIS IS AN ANDRE DEUTSCH BOOK

Published in 2019 by André Deutsch
An imprint of the Carlton Publishing Group
20 Mortimer Street
London W1T 3JW

Text © Roger Lederer 2019
Design © André Deutsch Limited 2019

A CIP catalogue for this book is available from the British Library.

ISBN 978 0 233 00607 9

Printed in Dubai

Editor: Isabel Wilkinson
Art Editor: Katie Baxendale
Designer: Anna Matos Melgaco
Picture Manager: Steve Behan
Production: Marion Storz

BIRDS

Ornithology and
The Great Bird Artists

Dr Roger J Lederer,
Ornithologist and Emeritus Professor of Biological Sciences

ANDRE
DEUTSCH

CONTENTS

7. ART AND SCIENCE OVERLAP 118

As exploration of the natural world expanded, artists became important observers. Comparing species and varieties required artists to put more than one species on a page, and scientific monographs on specific bird groups became more common.

8. BROADER APPEAL 144

The skills of artists, the variety of their styles, their publications, and their reach to communities outside of the art world stoked the public's interest both in birds and art.

9. BIRD ART SUPPORTS BIRDS 172

When the environmental movement began in earnest in the latter half of the twentieth century, people noticed that bird habitats were disappearing and bird numbers declining. Artists helped to increase public awareness of these environmental issues.

10. ORNITHOLOGICAL ART EXPANDS 196

Bird field guides and illustrated books maintain their popularity but artists are also producing novel, creative and bizarre bird art that continues to enthral and inspire.

INTRODUCTION

Birds have been the subjects of art for at least 40,000 years, from the time when our earliest ancestors carved or painted images of feathered creatures. Over the centuries, as we discovered more of their world and as attitudes toward them changed, so artistic representations of birds changed. This book is a reflection of the work of some 40 bird-oriented artists, from the seventeenth century to the present, and shows the effects that ornithological knowledge and attitudes towards birds have had on the evolution of such artwork.

Myth and symbol

From earliest history, birds featured in our folklore, myths, and symbols. Ancient Egyptians personified many of their gods as birds. Ancient Greek pottery displayed bird images on water jugs, bowls, and cups. The Hopi Indians of northwestern Arizona used figures of birds or feathers on their pottery, sand figures, and wooden tables. Before the seventeenth century, birds were symbols of spiritual guidance for many cultures. The finch represented a soul rising to heaven, the peacock everlasting life, the crow wicked thoughts, the owl wisdom, and the vulture greed and corruption.

Some birds attracted more attention than others. Ravens were associated with myths, folktales, and art. In the book of Genesis in the Bible, Noah releases a raven from the ark after the flood to determine whether the waters have receded. Native Americans believed the raven to be a bearer of magic and messages from the cosmos. The European goldfinch was often pictured in medieval paintings as representing the resurrection of Christ. The gold colour in the wings, the red face and cheeks, and its penchant for thistle seeds became religious symbols.

LEFT: Common moorhen, mosaic floor in the Villa of the Birds in Alexandria, Egypt.

OPPOSITE: Archibald Thorburn, *Peacock and Peacock Butterfly*, 1917.

Ornithology and illustration

Bird illustration in Europe may have begun with *De Arte Venandi cum Avibus* (*On the Art of Hunting with Birds*), written by Frederick II, *c.*1245. Birds were drawn in the margins in colour to enrich the text. Perhaps the first book of natural history that illustrated birds was *Buch der Natur* (*The Book of Nature*), assembled by Konrad von Megenberg around 1480.

In the latter part of the fifteenth century, woodcuts became popular, especially after the advent of printing. The first bird book illustrated by woodcuts was a seven-volume work, *L'Histoire de la Nature des Oyseaux* (*The History of the Nature of Birds*), by the Frenchman Pierre Belon, in 1555. In 1557 the Swiss Conrad Gessner published *Historiae Animalium* (*Histories of the Animals*), with 217 woodcuts. From 1599 to 1603, the Italian Ulisse Aldrovandi published a far

ABOVE: Frans Snyders,
Larder with a Servant,
1635–40.

OPPOSITE: Illustrations
from Francis Willughby's
*The Ornithology of Francis
Willughby: In Three Books
Wherein all the Birds
Hitherto Known* (1678).

longer book, grouping birds by their food, behaviour, or habitat. All three works were significant efforts at ornithology and illustration; Aldrovandi's book, in spite of substantial errors, was a standard reference for a hundred years. Volcher Coiter, a Dutch anatomist, dissected birds; he proposed a classification system, *De Differentiis Avium*, based on internal anatomy, and established a connection between birds' beaks and feeding habits.

During the Renaissance there were many paintings with realistic-appearing birds, albeit unnaturally set. Melchior d'Hondecoeter's *The Menagerie* shows several birds and two monkeys perched on an old wall. Frans Snyders's *Larder with a Servant* is typical of bird paintings of the era – a swan laid out with other game in preparation for a feast. Wild birds of many species graced the dinner table during this era.

The seventeenth century saw an increased number of menageries, including aviaries with exotic and rare birds kept by royalty and men of means. Giovanni Pietro Olina, an Italian naturalist, published writings on the nature and characteristics of songbirds in his 1622 book *Uccelliera, overo discorso della natura, e proprieta di diversi uccelli* (*Aviary, or nature's speech and the properties of different birds*).

Callidrys
nigra.
The Knot.

Rotknuʃʃel.
an Avis pugnax
fœm.

Cinclus Bellonij

Avis pugnax mas
A Ruffe

Matkneltzell.

Avis pugnax fœmina.
The Reeve.

In 1657 John Johnston published *Historia Naturalis de Avibus Libri* in Frankurt, the illustrations produced through the copper-plate engraving process – the main form of reproduction until the nineteenth century. His illustrations of birds were only roughly accurate, however, and included both bats and mythical creatures.

Francis Willughby and John Ray, in the late seventeenth century, published *Ornithologiae*, advocating a new way of classifying birds, by observation and description rather than accepted word; this might have been the first field guide.

Between 1729 and 1747 Mark Catesby, an English naturalist, published his *Natural History of Carolina, Florida and the Bahama Islands*, the first published account of the flora and fauna of North America. It included 220 plates of birds and other animals as well as plants and was, perhaps, the beginning of realistic representations of birds in their natural environment.

The late eighteenth century saw a great interest in the development of avian classification schemes. Georges-Louis Leclerc, Comte de Buffon's nine-volume *Histoire Naturelle des Oiseaux* and Mathurin-Jacques Brisson's six-volume *Ornithologie* were both significant, splendidly illustrated works. Buffon felt that groups such as genus and species were only figments of the human mind and that animals ought to be classified by how useful they were to humans. Brisson's treatise was much closer to the scheme devised by Swedish physician, botanist, and zoologist Carl Linnaeus, but never received much consideration. Linnaeus's taxonomic system ultimately became universally accepted.

John James Audubon made bird paintings famous with his life-size prints of almost 500 bird species. These are realistic to a great degree, although Audubon worked with dead specimens that he shot and mounted in a wire frame, not always in the most natural pose.

Proper classification continued to be a focus in ornithology in the nineteenth century, especially with exotic birds being brought to Europe and the United States from strange lands. Artists such as Elizabeth Gould and Prideaux John Selby were setting standards for what bird illustration should be. Comparing bird species was possible only if the artwork was scientifically accurate. Louis Agassiz Fuertes and Bruno Liljefors produced bird art that was not only visually appealing but reflected scientific information.

Seeing and technology

As photographic and printing equipment and techniques improved, so did the art, both for scientific illustration and for public consumption. A milestone in bird painting was reached with Roger Tory Peterson's *Field Guide to the Birds*, published in 1934. He set a style of accurate representations of birds and a format for field guides that still hold today.

In more recent years some enormously talented bird artists have produced art that shows incredible detailing of feathers, scales, and eye colour: David Allen Sibley is the Roger Tory Peterson of today; Elizabeth Butterworth paints and draws whole birds and their parts in minute, photographic-quality detail; Raymond Harris-Ching puts finely drawn birds in unique circumstances; and Janet Turner fills the entire canvas with birds.

Gallina Africana, & Numidica, en Latin: Poulle de la Guinee, en Francoys.

Along with different styles of bird art came changes in the field of ornithology. Preserving birds and placing them in lifelike positions proved to be a boon to artists and naturalists. Microscopes allowed the close examination of feathers, beaks and bones. Looking glasses – binoculars – were invented and improved, so birds could be studied in the wild. Advances in taxonomy allowed accurate naming, and enabled the relationships between species to be clarified. Aristotle recognized about 123 species of birds; today we know of 10,000 or so across the world, and we understand their form and function.

As science evolved and new species were discovered, birds began to be seen differently. They were still hunted for food and sport, kept as pets, and domesticated for their flesh, feathers, and eggs, but we now see them as an integral part of our environment. Artists, in reflecting the natural state of birds, remind us how the environment is changing. For example, in the 1960s peregrine falcons and bald eagles were the poster birds for the damage that DDT was doing to bird populations. Even today, the popularity of avian art is a testimony to our ongoing fascination for these colourful, musical masters of the air.

Chapter One

FLEMISH BAROQUE ARTISTS 1580–1700

Flemish Baroque art, characterized by bold colours and expressive detail, was produced in the southern Netherlands, from about 1585 to 1700. The most eminent artists of the period were Peter Paul Rubens, who was a potent influence on other European painters, and Jan Brueghel the Elder, who collaborated with Rubens on some works.

Frans Snyders was perhaps the most noted animal painter. He worked extensively with Rubens and painted large hunting scenes, a genre that helped to define the Flemish Baroque style. Carel Fabritius, a former pupil of Rembrandt, painted one of the most striking studies of a bird ever produced: *The Goldfinch*, in which Baroque style is pared down to provide the portrait of an individual creature. Melchior d'Hondecoeter specialized in painting birds – both the waterfowl and game birds he saw around him, and exotic specimens brought from Africa and Asia.

Parrots are a foundation of seventeenth-century Dutch paintings as they were exotic, beautiful, and rare. More than just showy, they were treasured companions

PREVIOUS PAGE: Rembrandt, *Self-portrait with Bittern*, 1639.

ABOVE: Peter Paul Rubens, *Tiger, Lion and Leopard Hunt*, c.1616.

OPPOSITE: Jan Brueghel the Elder, *Flowers in a Wooden Vessel*, 1606–07.

ABOVE: Peter Paul
Rubens, together with
Jan Bruegel, *The Vision
of Saint Hubert*, 1617.
Rubens may have
contracted out the
painting of animals and
plants to others such as
Frans Snyders.

OPPOSITE: Caspar
Netscher, *A Woman
Feeding a Parrot, with a
Page*, 1666.

and provided Dutch painters with a chance for creativity. They were often included
in portraits and almost always with a woman, perhaps because they can be trained
to talk, which is itself a miracle, just like the virgin who gave birth to Christ.

History painting was viewed as the most important genre from about the
sixteenth to the nineteenth century. The subject matter, from classical history,
mythology, and the Bible, typically depicted an important event or action. Other
forms of painting that developed in Antwerp were gallery and collection painting
– the painting of collectibles ensconced in a wall cabinet or on a bookshelf – plus
flower painting, still lifes, and hunting scenes. Pantry scenes were also common,
exhibiting dead game ready to be prepared for the table.

All these natural history specimens were simply just curiosities and subjects
for artwork until Francis Willughby and John Ray decided to examine them.
Before the middle of the seventeenth century, works of natural history were
overwrought, unwieldy, full of misinformation and irrelevant facts. Willughby
and his Cambridge tutor, Ray, decided to study, dissect and describe every known
bird (about 500 at the time), checking and verifying the information put forth
by their predecessors. Their intent and result was the orderly and meaningful
classification of birds. With the publication of *The Ornithology of Francis
Willughby* (1676), later extensively expanded by John Ray, ornithology came to be
a science. The first ornithology textbook, it was initially produced in Latin, as it
was intended for scholars, with an English version printed a year later. It remained
an authoritative text for around 200 years.

FRANS SNYDERS
Flemish, 1579–1657

Frans Snyders, painting in Antwerp, studied under Pieter Bruegel the Younger. He went on to become part of a vibrant group of artists, including Jan Brueghel the Elder and Peter Paul Rubens. In 1602 Snyders became a master painter in the Antwerp Painters' Guild.

Snyders's initial subjects were still lifes of fruit and flowers and other objects, with an emphasis on the play of light. Soon his speciality became the depiction of animals among and around still lifes. He was often employed by Rubens to paint still lifes and animals in Rubens's paintings.

His paintings display birds and mammals – or occasionally fish, reptiles, or invertebrates – hung on a wall, over a hearth, or from hooks on a wooden rack. Other creatures might be laid across a table, perhaps with their head dangling over the edge or draped over a fruit or vegetable. Sometimes, as in his fish market paintings, dozens of fish and a few other denizens of the aquatic world would be haphazardly piled on one another in a slimy morass.

In the midst of some of these scenes, Snyders introduced portraits of living animals such as dogs, monkeys, or parrots. Usually the animals were shown just observing, sniffing, and hoping for a free meal. In one portrayal of a basket of fruit, a few dead game animals, and some vegetables, a monkey and a squirrel are surreptitiously attempting to grab a few pieces of fruit while a cat looks on, more interested in the dead animals on the table. Many of the deceased creatures on the table were birds.

In the sixteenth century, birds were accorded a rank relating to their perceived "nobility". Eagles, hawks, and falcons stood higher than other birds. Second in line were the birds that ate insects and other invertebrates: cuckoo, nightingale, parrot, and pheasant, for example. Water birds that ate vegetation, such as geese, swans, and ducks, came third; and the seed-eating songbirds ranked last.

In some of Snyders's paintings the mute swan is a centrepiece, with its heavy white body splayed across a table and its long neck and head draped over the edge. The bird may have represented purity, or perhaps its colour and size balanced the picture.

Of all the birds Snyders depicted in pantry or kitchen scenes, the grey partridge featured most frequently, and it was a rarity for the swan to appear. Of the songbirds represented in his paintings, the chaffinch is the most popular, followed

RIGHT: Frans Snyders, *Market Scene on a Quay*, c.1635–40. Shows the typical pose of a mute swan with the body on the table and the neck and head hanging over.

by the bullfinch. The presence or absence of a particular bird species at a table may have to do with the ranking of birds or it might just have been an artistic decision to balance the colour of the painting. The white-tailed eagle is found only twice in Snyders's paintings, perhaps because they were among the noblest of birds and, of course, not a favoured food item. The kingfisher appears in some gastronomic scenes by Snyders, but as it was not eaten much, it was probably included purely for its iridescent plumage.

His *Still Life with Grey Parrot* features a naturalistically rendered, live grey parrot surveying a collection of dead game birds and other food. The bird communicates status, health, and wealth via successful international trade. Pheasants and partridges are often seen, perhaps reflecting the success of a hunt, a preference for these birds as food, or just because their detailed plumage, like that of the peacock, demonstrates the artist's skills. Scarlet macaws are common in Snyders's other paintings, perhaps for their contrasting colours.

Snyders's most famous painting may be *Concert of Birds*. The painting presents a colourful diversity of birds surrounding an owl as concertmaster holding a musical score. The theme is taken from Aesop's *The Owl and the Birds*, but it is also linked to a Dutch saying, "Every bird sings the way he knows how", or "Every bird sings with the beak it has been given", which has been interpreted as reflecting nature's organization. Snyders's influence made this theme popular in seventeenth-century Flemish art.

LEFT: Frans Snyders, *Concert of Birds*, c.1629–30. The owl is trying to organize an unruly bunch of birds in order to make a chorus. The painting presents a colourful variety of birds paying attention to an owl that perches on a branch holding an open musical score. The theme is taken from Aesop's fable *The Owl and the Birds*. There are several versions and copies of this painting.

ABOVE: Frans Snyders, *Fish Market (Tribute Money?)*, c.1621. This painting shows a seemingly endless variety of the inhabitants of rivers, seas, and lakes, depicted by Snyders with almost biological precision. The human figures seem to be bargaining.

CAREL PIETERSZ FABRITIUS
Flemish, 1622–54

Fabritius's family name may, appropriately, have come from the Latin faber, *meaning artist or craftsman.*

OPPOSITE: Carel Fabritius,
The Goldfinch, 1654.
Perhaps one of the
most famous of all bird
paintings. *The Goldfinch*
is a trompe l'oeil painting
that depicts the bird on
top of its feeder, to which
it is chained. Goldfinches
in the seventeenth century
were popular because they
could be trained to pull up
a small bucket to obtain
water. The Dutch name
of the painting is *Het
puttertje*, which translates
as "the little weller".

A precocious artist, Fabritius moved to Amsterdam to work with Rembrandt in 1641; he is considered to be one of Rembrandt's best students, with his own distinct style. Fabritius had no previous art training, but his father and three of his brothers were painters, so he had considerable exposure to the craft. Fabritius worked in Rembrandt's studio until 1650, after his wife and two children died, then moved to Delft, the home of Vermeer; some people suggest he was an influence on Vermeer.

Fabritius left only a small body of work during his short life. His most famous painting is *The Goldfinch*, painted in 1654, the year he died. In this simple yet striking piece, the bird's red facial markings and black and white splashes of plumage contrast with the radiant light on the creamy tan wall behind it.

The European goldfinch is a small songbird native to Europe, North Africa, and western Asia. Goldfinches have long been domesticated; 2,000 years ago Pliny mentioned their ability to perform tricks. In the painting the bird sits on top of its cage, secured by a thin chain. In the seventeenth century it was popular to capture goldfinches and teach them various tricks. In the wild, the birds hold thistles with their feet as they extract seeds; this ability was exploited by their human stewards. The birds would be tethered by a chain to their nest box or food box and trained to pull up a chain or string to which was attached a bucket filled with seeds or water. The Dutch title of the painting, *Het puttertje*, means "the little weller".

At least 486 devotional pictures containing goldfinches were created during the Renaissance, with the bird almost always in the hands of the Christ child. It seems that the goldfinch appearing in pictures of the Madonna and Christ child, such as *Madonna of the Goldfinch*, by Raphael about 1506, is predicting the crucifixion. The bird is associated with the Passion and Christ's crown of thorns because the bird feeds among thorns that encircle Jesus's head, the bird's red face coming from Jesus's blood. What is unusual about Fabritius's painting is that it is a portrait of one bird – not as background or as one of a group of live or dead birds, but a focus on one individual bird. The painting resides in the Mauritshuis in The Hague.

Fabritius tragically died young in an explosion in a gunpowder storage facility in Delft in 1654 at the age of 32. It is likely that most of his works were destroyed with him.

C FABRITIVS 1654

MELCHIOR D'HONDECOETER
Dutch, 1636–95

A painter of animals, and one of several generations of painters in his family, Melchior d'Hondecoeter is notable for the liveliness with which he painted birds.

He began his studies with his father and later with his uncle after his father died. When d'Hondecoeter was in his early twenties, he moved to The Hague and became a member of the painters' academy, moving to Amsterdam four years later. He began his career by producing sea pieces, scenes with fish and other marine creatures. Later he switched to birds and became well known as a bird painter.

His first paintings were still lifes of dead game and hunting accessories with a live bird or two viewing the scene; d'Hondecoeter admired Frans Snyders's works and was probably influenced by Snyders's still lifes. Later, d'Hondecoeter painted live birds, mainly barnyard species such as hens and turkeys, in a classical or Italianate setting. A number of paintings portrayed cockfights, sometimes with other birds, even pigeons and ducks, entering the fray. Exotic birds featured in subsequent years, the subjects a mixture of chickens and ducks with pelicans, cranes, and cassowaries.

Melchior d'Hondecoeter was apparently the only painter in the Netherlands who seemed to appreciate birds as living beings with feelings. Other painters before him seemed only to see the colours and to use birds as additions to the landscape; d'Hondecoeter made them the focus of his painting.

In *The Crow Exposed* he demonstrates his ability to show the details of each figure. The story of the picture is that the god Jupiter declares that he will anoint the most beautiful bird as king of all birds. The crow, being black, fears he has no chance, so he finds the fallen feathers of colourful birds and dons them. As Jupiter is just about to crown the crow as king, the other birds attack the crow and expose him. The feathers and beaks of the birds all have different shades of red or pink, colours that connect the scattered birds to each other and to the centre with the bright red rooster's head.

D'Hondecoeter often composed his paintings by putting some figures in the centre foreground, with others entering from the sides. He was skilled at depicting the exact likeness of birds but also giving the birds human-like expressions.
In his painting *Birds around a Balustrade, with the Amsterdam City Hall in the Background*, the main figure, the peacock, looks very much as if he is berating the owl on a perch while the peacock's mate, the peahen, keeps a low profile; the owl looks taken aback at the verbal abuse coming from the peacock. The smaller birds are hardly noticeable and do not pay much attention to this interaction.

OPPOSITE: Melchior d'Hondecoeter, *A Hunter's Bag near a Tree Stump with a Magpie*, c.1688. Also known as the *Contemplative Magpie*; the magpie seems to be confused by all these dead birds at his feet.

ABOVE: Melchior d'Hondecoeter, *The Crow Exposed*, 1680. Melchior d'Hondecoeter was famous for painting a variety of birds realistically and with liveliness. He is considered one of the most accomplished painters of varying and exotic birds.

The Menagerie, painted about 1690, shows a number of exotic birds – sulphur-crested cockatoos from Australia, a ring-necked parakeet from sub-Saharan Africa or southern Asia, a grey parrot from central Africa, a northern cardinal from north America, a few other smaller birds, and a couple of monkeys. All of the animals seem wary of something either in front or to the side of the painting. The picture exemplifies the emotions d'Hondecoeter was able to imbue in his subjects.

Many of d'Hondecoeter's canvases were originally designed to hang above fireplaces and doors in well-to-do neighbourhoods in Amsterdam.

OPPOSITE: Melchior d'Hondecoeter, *Birds Around a Balustrade, with the Amsterdam City Hall in the Background*, c.1670. The peacock seems to be talking to the owl while the rest of the birds seem uninterested.

Chapter Two

EARLY
ENGLISH ARTISTS
1626–1716

———

The depicting of animals in art goes back to the early representations of creatures on the walls of caves, especially in regard to hunting. As art evolved, animal representations took a back seat to religious, historical, and portraiture genres. Artists of these forms would often collaborate with *animaliers* (animal painters) to add creatures to their work such as a pet dog sitting on a hearth or birds flying in the background.

Portraiture was the dominant form of painting in England from the Renaissance until the late 1800s, when photography began to become the more popular form of memorialization. During the era of portrait painting, the prosperity of the ruling and merchant classes provided the means for many artists to make their living painting portraits and caricatures. However, by the close of the seventeenth century, *animaliers* had developed a reputation of their own. The relationship people had with their pets and the popularity of hunting increased the demand for animal art. This was especially true in England. During this period, the British taste for animal and bird paintings was captured most notably by Francis Barlow, seen as Britain's first wildlife painter; by the Hungarian Jakob Bogdani, who became the foremost bird painter in England; and by the self-taught Marmaduke Cradock, who focused his attention on native domestic and wild birds, often drawn from life.

Where avian subjects were concerned, in the second half of the 1600s, still lifes of dead game birds and mammals conveyed an aristocratic image of country life. Exotic birds generated interest as explorers and traders returned from foreign continents with unusual forms. Colourful birds such as parrots and pheasants were in demand for menageries or as pets, and artists were provided with a cornucopia of new subjects.

Unfortunately many of the birds died in transport, and there was no efficient method of preservation. If a live specimen was not available, artists painted from memory, mimicked previous artwork, or used birds preserved in liquid, which often changed their colouration. In addition, without a model artists were left to rely on the description of others, or their imagination, to pose the bird in what they thought was a realistic posture. For example, Jakob Bogdani's main subject in *Flamingo and Other Birds in a Landscape*, with its overly long neck and stiff legs, looks more like a caricature than a real bird.

Coursing ye Hare

A Cock who to a neighbouring Dunghill tries, | Cry'd he — a Barly corne wou'd please me more,
Finding a gemme that 'mongst the Rubish lyes. | Then all the Treasures on the eastern shore.

Morall

Gay nonsense does the noysy fopling please,
Beyond the noblest Arts and Sciences.

FAB. I.
De Gallo Gallinaceo.

Gallus gallinaceus dum armato pede sterquilinium dissipando
disjicit invenit Gemmam, Quid, inquiens, rem tam fulgurantem
reperio? Si Gemmarius invenisset, lætabundus exultaret, quippe qui
scivit pretium; mihi quidem nulli est usui, nec magni æstimo, unum et-
enim Hordei granum est mihi longè pretiosius, quam omnes Gemmæ,
quamvis ad Invidiam micent Diei, opprobriumque Solis.

MORALE.

Homines sunt Naturâ tam depravati, ut ad perituras Divitias &
fallacia Gaudia citiùs feruntur, quàm ad Nobiles Virtutum Dotes,
quæ non solùm Corpus Honore afficiunt, sed Animum etiam & cælo
Beant.   FABLE II.

FRANCIS BARLOW

English, c. 1626–1704

Francis Barlow was a painter, etcher, and one of the most active book illustrators and printmakers of the seventeenth century. He is best known for designing 110 woodcuts for John Ogilby's 1665 edition of Aesop's Fables *and for being the British "father of sporting paintings".*

Born in Lincolnshire, Barlow moved to London at an early age and was apprenticed for three years with a portrait painter before he struck out on his own. The usual time of apprenticeship is seven years, so it seems that Barlow had the financial means to pursue his own interests, painting flora and fauna. While he was still an apprentice, the royal hunting laws were abolished after the death of Charles I (but reinstated later), so people could hunt and fish

OPPOSITE: Francis Barlow, illustration for the first fable, from *Aesop's Fables* (1665). Translation: A rooster with his well-equipped foot was tossing up the dung heap and scattering it around. He found a jewel and said, "What's the point of me finding such a shiny thing? If a jeweller had found it, he would have jumped with joy, since a jeweller knows what a jewel is worth; for me, however, the thing is of no use at all, and I do not value it highly; in fact, one grain of barley is far more precious to me than all the jewels, even though the jewels sparkle so as to arouse the envy of the daylight and the reproach of the sun".

RIGHT: *The Decoy*, Francis Barlow's allegory from the 1670s on the threat posed to England by Roman Catholicism. The figures of the hawk and heron are repeated in other paintings in the same pose.

TOP: Francis Barlow, *An Owl being Mobbed by Other Birds*, 1673. This is a rather common motif over the centuries.

ABOVE: F Place after Francis Barlow, *An owl being mocked by other birds*, c.1690. Rather than mocking, the other birds are mobbing the owl in order to scare it away as it is a predator.

as much as they pleased. Barlow learned about hunting and managed to collect some specimens of birds and mammals. Early drawings in pen and brown ink, such as a drawing of a horseman with his hound attacking a deer, reflect Barlow's knowledge of hunting.

Although Barlow never left the British Isles, he was apparently influenced by Flemish painters such as Breughel and Snyders (see page 18). As he built on still life and hunting themes, he started painting realistic pictures of animals freshly killed or alive. He was one of the first bird artists to assimilate animals into a naturalistic landscape. Falconry was common among royalty, so he often included raptors – eagles, owls, and hawks.

In 1658 Barlow published *Birds and Fowles of Various Species*, which included a number of illustrations with various feathered creatures. In one, four peacocks warily eye a southern cassowary and an ostrich while a monkey, included to represent folly, looks on. Barlow drew the birds from life as peacocks were common and ostriches and cassowaries were part of King Charles II's menagerie in St James's Park, London. Barlow eventually became the leading animal illustrator in seventeenth-century England, decorating the ceilings of castles, and was even commissioned to work on Westminster Abbey.

By the end of the sixteenth century, copper-plate engraving had mostly replaced woodcuts, but Barlow utilized both. He apparently kept a stock of "models":

drawings and paintings of flowers and animals to which he could refer for information. This allowed him to use the same or a similar representation of an animal in different paintings. Some repetition of these motifs can be seen in a flying mallard, a heron taking off, and swallows, both perched and aerial. The books of models that he produced were also sold to naturalists home and abroad. His first model book of birds, self-published, included 15 birds of one related kind or individual species set in an appropriate landscape.

Barlow was certainly highly regarded for his technical skill, but it would be a stretch to consider many of his works a close representation of reality. Some of his birds are misshapen or posed awkwardly, and detail is often lacking. Some of his paintings lack the depth and vivid colours of Dutch works. Even composition was not a strong point: animals in his works tend to be cluttered together. But Barlow, Britain's first wildlife painter, began a tradition that continued for many years and reached its peak work with George Stubbs, known for his horse paintings, in the late eighteenth century.

EARLY ENGLISH ARTISTS 1626–1716

JAKOB BOGDANI
Hungarian/English, 1658–1724

At the age of 26, Jakob Bogdani (or Bogdany) moved to Amsterdam from the city of his birth, Eperies, at that time part of the Kingdom of Hungary (now located in Slovakia).

While living in Amsterdam he was a painter of still-lifes and probably worked with or at least learned from Melchior d'Hondecoeter (see page 24), who lived in the city at the same time. He shared a room with a German Baroque flower painter, Ernst Stuven, and no doubt learned from him as well. Bogdani's earliest works were flowers in the Dutch tradition, such as *Fruit-piece with Stone Vase* and *Flower Piece with Parrot*.

Four years later Bogdani moved to London, where his still lifes and bird paintings were well received, as Dutch art was popular there. He painted in the court of Queen Anne, who encouraged him, and a number of his paintings were accepted into the Royal Collection. Admiral George Churchill, brother of John Churchill, the Duke of Marlborough, was one of his patrons. He painted several

OPPOSITE: Jakob Bogdani, *Still Life with Parrot, Fruit and Dead Birds*, c.1700.

RIGHT: Jakob Bogdani, *Fruit in a Pewter Bowl with a Parrot*, date unknown.

OPPOSITE ABOVE: Jakob
Bogdani, *Variety of Ducks
by a Pool*, date unknown.
All the ducks are domestic,
some showing a poofy crest
on the head.

OPPOSITE BELOW: Jakob
Bogdani, *Cockerels and
Pigeons*, date unknown.

ABOVE: Jakob Bogdani,
*Two Macaws, a Cockatoo,
and a Jay, with Fruit*, 1710.
The parrots demonstrate
the access Bogdani had to
the Duke of Marlborough's
aviary.

pictures for George Churchill, which show collections of exotic animals, often with a
background of classical architecture, such as *Two Macaws, a Cockatoo and a Jay, with
Fruit* (1710).

George Churchill established an aviary at Windsor Park, which served as the source
of subjects for some of Bogdani's paintings. After he gained access to the aviary in
1703, his interest in birds increased. His bird paintings included exotic bird species
such as macaws, cockatoos, flamingoes, toucans and curassows. Often, still lifes were
highlighted with the addition of a bright red bird such as a northern cardinal or a king
parrot. When he placed a number of birds together, he often mixed these exotic species
with more familiar domestic birds. He became the leader of the avian genre in England
and was much in demand, becoming a wealthy man as a result.

Bogdani's *Two Iceland Falcons*, one of his most famous works, was an exception to
his typical subjects in being a more intimate, muted portrait of just the two birds. In
the medieval era, the gyrfalcon was considered a royal bird, reserved for kings and
nobles in European falconry. A king could fly a gyrfalcon; an earl would fly a peregrine
falcon; a yeoman could have a goshawk; the sparrowhawk (Eurasian sparrowhawk) was
reserved for priests; and servants would have a kestrel (common kestrel).

Bogdani's paintings were largely influenced by Churchill's aviary, but he also used
stuffed birds from his personal collection. The idea of painting large-scale canvases full
of exotic birds in a formal setting is sometimes attributed to Melchior d'Hondecoeter
(see page 24), who probably influenced Jakob Bogdani. In turn, Bogdani influenced the
painter Marmaduke Cradock (see page 40).

MARMADUKE CRADOCK

English, 1660–1716

Born in Somerset, England, Cradock began his working life as an apprentice house painter after moving to London. Later, he embarked on a career as an animal artist.

Self-taught, he styled his work after Melchior d'Hondecoeter (see page 24) and Jakob Bogdani (see page 36) and closely followed Francis Barlow (see page 32), not in style but in subject matter. Cradock worked independently for dealers who sold his works, as he did not wish to be employed by someone whose birth and fortune might restrict his artistic freedom; he supposed that any patron would "confine his genius to their fancy". There are a number of sketches by Cradock in the British Museum indicating that he drew from life. However, there are only three known works actually signed by him.

Several artists of this age preferred to paint exotic species for their colour and fanciful plumage, but Cradock preferred to paint domestic birds and common wildfowl of the area. He often included some classic architecture in the far background. However, he did include peacocks in his work. Peacocks, more properly "peafowl", are native to Southern Asia and Malaysia. Apparently the Chinese were the first to import and domesticate these birds over 4,000 years ago. They have become familiar in various cultures and represent values such as glory,

LEFT: Marmaduke Cradock, *A Turkey, Peacock, and Chickens in a Landscape*, date unknown.

RIGHT: Marmaduke Cradock, *Peacocks, Doves, Turkeys, Chickens and Ducks by a Classical Ruin*, c.1700.

incorruptibility, immortality, vanity, and luxury. Christians believed that the "eyes" of the tail feathers represent the all-seeing eye of God.

Cradock's *Peacocks, Doves, Turkeys, Chickens and Ducks by a Classical Ruin*, painted about 1700, includes pigeons, a jay, a partridge, and two turkeys, but the male peacock is clearly the focus. The bird species are clearly identifiable, as they are realistically represented. The jay seems to be giving an alarm call while the rock pigeon appears to be evading a potentially dangerous situation. According to the Tate Gallery, "Cradock seems to be using the natural world as a moral commentary on human life, the dovecote's predator and the peril it brings acting as a moral check to the

EARLY ENGLISH ARTISTS 1626–1716

outward harmony and worldly vanity of the scene". Interestingly, there are at least two other paintings by other artists, with the same title. The work by Dutch artist Jan Victors was painted c.1640–50, so may have inspired Cradock's work. The painting by Italian Giovanni Crivelli of the mid-eighteenth century bears a close resemblance to Cradock's.

The peacock, although realistic, appears in the same pose in other works by Cradock, indicating that he used a stuffed specimen or just copied an earlier piece. Cradock made at least three versions of this subject, and this is one of the three known works signed by him. Another signed piece is a metal teapot that he painted in colour, now in the Victoria and Albert Museum in London.

73

Chapter Three

NATURAL HISTORY
1680–1806

———

Natural history is the observation of nature. Roman naturalist Pliny the Elder, in his *Naturalis Historia*, defined natural history as including any aspect of the natural world, from plants and animals to the structures of the Earth and the movements of the stars. During the Renaissance in Europe, there was a new explosion of information about the natural world. The advent of printing saw encyclopedic works created, including the latest discoveries retrieved by explorations – even if these were unsubstantiated. Griffins, harpies, and unicorns might have been noted, for example, and the migration of birds was explained by their flying to the moon for the winter. But slowly, what we now know as science began to emerge; reality was replacing mythology. Zoology and botany grew substantially, largely due to accurate descriptions of species and their classification into discrete categories.

Ornithology arose out of natural history as new birds were discovered and collected; then those collections needed organization and illustration. It began in the mid-seventeenth century with *The Ornithology of Willughby*, the first ornithology text. In France, George-Louis Leclerc, Comte de Buffon, released his *Histoire naturelle des oiseaux* in nine volumes from 1770 to 1783. He described about 2,000 species, but disagreed with Swedish naturalist Carl Linnaeus, the father of modern taxonomy (the science of classifying organisms), because Buffon thought birds ought to be classified on the basis of behaviour and habitat and not anatomy. Mathurin Jacques Brisson, a French zoologist, published his *Ornithologie* in 1790, a six-volume work with more scientific and descriptive details than either Linnaeus or Buffon, but it faded into history.

Art made ornithology possible. Without accurate graphic depictions of whole birds as well as dissected ones, classification and information exchange would have been near impossible. Artists painted from life, if they could, but that was often difficult, so they depended on dead specimens. Taxidermy was common but preservation was not, so skins would deteriorate quickly.

Explorers brought unusual creatures, dead and alive, to Europe from exotic places: there was no lack of subjects. However, there was a lack of context. Compare Mark Catesby, who thought about ecological concepts as he etched and painted, to George Edwards, considered the "father of British ornithology" mainly because he was a proficient artist, and to Aert Schouman, who seems to have been almost totally disconnected from the ecological world but again was an excellent artist.

PREVIOUS PAGE: George Edwards, *Otis tarda, the Great Bustard*, from *A Natural History of Uncommon Birds, Vol. 2* (1747).

ABOVE: Mark Catesby, *American Oystercatcher*, c.1731–43, from *The Natural History of Carolina, Florida, and the Bahama Islands Vol. 1* (1731–43).

OPPOSITE: Aert Schouman, *A Great White Crested Cockatoo*, date unknown. A caged bird, easy to observe.

MARK CATESBY
English, 1682/3–1749

English-born Mark Catesby studied natural history in London, and moved to Virginia in 1712. His early interest in botanical specimens led to his appointment as a plant collector in the Carolinas on behalf of the Royal Society.

He did little painting and returned to England in 1719. In 1722 he made his second trip to America, supported by wealthy noblemen. This time, in the Low Country (along the coast) of South Carolina, he collected, studied, and painted the local flora and fauna, extending his trips to Georgia and the Bahamas.

In 1726 Catesby returned to England. He spent the next 17 years preparing and publishing his *Natural History of Carolina, Florida and the Bahama Islands*, the first published account of the flora and fauna of North America. It included 220 copper-plate etchings, which he created, hand-coloured, and printed on large sheets of paper, of birds, reptiles and amphibians, fish, insects, and mammals, as well as plants. The book was admired and used as a reference by Benjamin Franklin, Thomas Jefferson, and others who were versed in natural history, indicating its importance as an illustrated natural history of America. Catesby's illustrations provided the kind of visual information that photography does today, and he was the first to include folio-sized drawings in a natural history book.

Catesby's emphasis was on botany because he realized the importance of plants in agriculture, food, and medicine. Almost as important, though, was his focus on birds, because he felt that they had the closest relationship to plants of any animals. On 5 March 1747, Catesby read a paper entitled "Of Birds of Passage" to the Royal Society in London, and he is now recognized as one of the first to describe bird migration, although his thesis was wrong. He surmised that the impetus for migration was food and that when birds migrated they would fly vertically until they were high enough to see their destination, and glide down.

Catesby mentions some correspondence that he had with a friend in Virginia who noticed birds he had never seen before. Catesby supposed that flora and fauna were in a state of flux and that the introduction of wheat, barley, and rice in the late seventeenth century had attracted foreign bird species. These "rice birds" and "wheat birds" as he called them, were most likely bobolinks.

Catesby's birds were pictured in realistic attitudes – an aggressive blue jay, an owl perched quizzically on a stump, a belted kingfisher with a fish in her mouth – but other aspects were not as realistic. A flamingo, a denizen of saltwater environs with a scarcity of trees, stands in front of a leafless tree. Another work features a "goatsucker", probably a nighthawk; this bird has weak feet and only preys on insects in mid-flight, but in Catesby's depiction the bird appears to be standing on the ground, about to gulp down its prey. The (black-billed) cuckoo of Carolina

ABOVE Mark Catesby, *The Chattering Plover and the Sorrel-Tree*, 1722–26. Clearly recognizable although posture and markings are imprecise.

OPPOSITE: Mark Catesby, *The Ivory-billed Woodpecker and Willow Oak*, date unknown. The bird is now considered extinct.

Magnolia Lauri folio, Subtus albicante.
The Sweet Flowring Bay.

Coccothraustes coeruleus.
The blew Grosbeak.

LEFT: Mark Catesby, *The Blew (Blue) Grosbeak and the Sweet Flowering Bay (Southern Magnolia)*, from *The Natural History of Carolina, Florida, and the Bahama Islands Vol. 1* (1731–43). Catesby's primary focus was botany because he understood the economic importance of plants. Only slightly less important was his focus on birds, which he felt had the closest relationship to plants of any animals.

OPPOSITE ABOVE: Mark Catesby, *The Blue Jay and the Bay-leaved Smilax*, c.1722–26. This is one of Catesby's reasonably realistic drawings; the colour is good although the colour of the face is not accurate.

OPPOSITE BELOW: Mark Catesby, *The Mock-bird and the Dogwood Tree* (now northern mockingbird), from *The Natural History of Carolina, Florida, and the Bahama Islands Vol. 1*. The posture is good but the characteristic white patch and wing bars are missing.

is too dark, and the red ring around the eye is missing. The mock-bird (northern mockingbird) is posed realistically but is brown instead of grey, and the distinctive white patches of the wings and wingbars are missing. He appears to have drawn an immature bird. Perspective was sometimes lost, as in the case of the passenger pigeon placed among overly large oak leaves.

Catesby was not an ornithologist, and he often devoted more effort to depicting plants than the animal that shared space on the paper, but nevertheless he is considered the founder of American ornithology. He set a new standard for avian art simply by painting animals along with plants, a style that dominates today's bird art.

Smilax lævis Lauri folio non Serrato, baccis nigris.

Pica cristata cærulea.
The crested Jay.

Cornus Florida.

Cornus mas &c.

Turdus minor &c.
The Mock-bird.

GEORGE EDWARDS
English, 1694–1773

Born in Essex, George Edwards was a voracious reader. After a mediocre business career in London, he travelled extensively through Europe, studying natural history.

ABOVE: George Edwards, *Upupa epops* (common hoopoe), from his *The Gleanings of Natural History, Vol. 3* (1764).

OPPOSITE: George Edwards, *Hahn's or Red-shouldered Macaw*, from *A Natural History of Uncommon Birds* (1743–51).

When he returned home he began to make coloured drawings of animals, which he sold for good prices. By the time he turned thirty, he was earning an income by teaching young ladies and gentlemen to draw. In the process he accumulated a large art portfolio that earned him an introduction to the Royal Society, whose president at that time was Sir Hans Sloane, naturalist and collector. (Sloane ultimately left a collection of 71,000 items to Britain, providing the beginning of London's British Museum and British Library.)

In 1733, Sloane recommended that George Edwards be appointed bedell (librarian) of the Royal College of Physicians. Edwards received a small salary, but more importantly, he had time to wade through many of the natural history works among the 8,000 volumes in the library and produce drawings that he sold for additional income.

George Edwards came to be known as "the father of British ornithology" for his extensive studies of birds. His most famous work is the four-volume *A Natural History of Uncommon Birds*, published from 1743 to 1751. That is the beginning of a very long title (*And of Some Other Rare and Undescribed Animals, Quadrupeds, Fishes, Insects, Exhibited in Two Hundred and Ten Copper-plates … etc.*) The animals were global in distribution – a "hooping" crane from Hudson's Bay, a "northern penguin" from Newfoundland (actually the now-extinct great auk) and birds-of-paradise from New Guinea. The most interesting has to be the dodo, which died out from the island of Mauritius in the seventeenth century. Edwards must have painted it from a preserved specimen. Strangely, he adds a guinea pig to the dodo plate; there were no native mammals on Mauritius, and to this day no guinea pigs live there, so presumably Edwards just included it for contrast.

Three supplements to his natural history were published in 1758, 1760, and 1764. Along with his original work, these seven volumes contained descriptions and engravings of more than 600 natural history subjects, most of which had not been described previously. Some of the descriptions of the birds give an idea of where he obtained these specimens; for example, Edwards writes of the European roller, "The bird from which my design was taken…, was shot on the Rocks of Gibraltar, and lent to Mr Catesby, in London, who obliged me with the use of it". If Edwards received stuffed specimens with no information, he would perch small birds on a branch of lichens and larger birds on a backdrop of water, having little or no idea of their natural habitat.

Although Edwards's illustrations leave something to be desired, he made careful and thorough descriptions of the specimens. In fact, Linnaeus used Edwards's

Geo Edwards Delin et Sculp

D 1755

229

The Brasilian Pie or Toucan. Drawn after Nature by Geo. Edwards Anno Dom 1754

238

G. Eduards ad viv. delin.

F. M. Seligman excudit.
Cum. Priv. Sac. Caes. Majestatis.
Nᵒ. 42. Vᵗᵉʳ Theil.

Joh. Sebast. Leitner sculps.

Penguin Arcticus.

Le Penguin du Nord.

detailed observations to name nearly 350 species of birds, many of them "type" specimens. (A type is a particular specimen on which the description of that species is based and to which the scientific name is attached.)

Edwards's bird paintings were an improvement on those of some earlier painters in that their poses were mainly realistic, but he seemed to have difficulty in portraying feathers in a convincing manner. A bird-of-paradise has a tail that looks like a sheaf of wheat, and his grey peacock-pheasant appears to be covered

ABOVE: George Edwards, *Northern Penguin* (actually the great auk), from *A Natural History of Uncommon Birds.*

OPPOSITE: George Edwards, *Toco Toucan*, from *A Natural History of Uncommon Birds.*

G. Edwards ad viv. delin.

Cum Priv. Sac. Caes. Majestatis.
Nº 84. VIIIᵗᵉʳ Theil

J. M. Seeligmann excudit

Dodo avis
Mus Africanus
Porçellus Guineenſis dictus.

Le Dodo et le Cochon d'Inde.

with hair rather than feathers. In his revision of Catesby's *Natural History* (1754)
the colours are too bright, not reflecting those in nature. Edwards has been
described as a "recorder of nature and not a gifted artist". However, one gets the
impression that, had cameras been available in his time, Edwards might have been
a great photographer.

Edwards was awarded the Copley Medal (the oldest and most prestigious award
by the Royal Society) in 1750 for outstanding achievement in the sciences.

OPPOSITE: George Edwards, *The Dodo* (posed with a guinea pig), from *A Natural History of Uncommon Birds*.

RIGHT: George Edwards, *King Bird of Paradise*, from *A Natural History of Uncommon Birds*. Not a very realistic portrait; the colour is especially bleak.

LESSER KING BIRD OF PARADISE.

Published July 31. 1802. by Harrison. & Co. N°. 108. Newgate Street.

AERT SCHOUMAN
Dutch, 1710–92

Born in Dordrecht in the Netherlands, Aert Schouman was apprenticed to artist Adriaen van der Burg at the age of 15. He initially painted biblical and mythological themes, and later decorative compositions with birds, then portraits and landscapes.

He took on his first art pupil in 1733 and continued teaching for the rest of his life as well as keeping a detailed diary of his professional life. He was prolific not only as a painter but as a glass engraver, printmaker, collector, and dealer, who produced still lifes, portraits, sketches, etchings, tapestries and wall hangings, and decorated objects such as fans and snuffboxes. A famous portrait is one of Cornelis van Lill, the Dordrecht art collector and patron, with his grandson and including the painter himself. He also painted a self portrait.

Schouman was inspired by earlier painters, especially d'Hondecoeter (see page 24), but developed a distinct style. He painted dead birds from collectors' cabinets, as well as those in aviaries. These "cabinets of curiosities" containing all manner of natural items were originally rooms, and later pieces of furniture, that served to make the owner a source of natural history information. In 1786, Schouman was commissioned by an estate to create seven painted wall hangings with all manner of birds painted on them. These were hung in a circle, to give viewers the impression that they were surrounded by nature.

Schouman painted birds he saw in the aviaries of the aristocracy. As a result, he often depicted birds from different continents together in the same tree: for example, one picture included a golden pheasant, native to forested mountain areas of China, next to a guineafowl, a resident of the savanna of sub-Saharan Africa. The painting has a forested background, but what appear to be palm trees are seen in the distance. In another work a whydah from Africa perches next to a cotinga of South America. Similarly, a widowbird from Africa is paired with a parrot from Asia. Nevertheless, Schouman's bird paintings are fairly true to life, although in many the plumages appear rumpled rather than showing sleek, smooth feathers. A watercolour entitled *Red-billed Toucan* (1748) shows the bird with two toes over the front of the branch and two toes behind – a keen observation of the bird's natural posture. However, the bill is bent in a sharp tip at the end, unlike that of the actual bird.

The golden pheasant appears in a number of Schouman's works, as do a couple of other pheasant species. Pheasants are spectacularly coloured, easy to keep in captivity, and not a particularly active species; spending nearly all of their time on the ground, they make good subjects for art studies. They are popular subjects even today. Similarly, other birds in captivity, such as ducks, geese, swans, chickens, and partridges, are easy to observe and paint. A similar argument applies to parrots, which are not usually very active, perching in the same place for long periods. Observing birds in nature is much more difficult, but to do so gives an artist a different perspective on the birds' environment and behaviour.

OPPOSITE: Aert Schouman, *Red-billed Toucan*, 1748.

ABOVE: Aert Schouman, *Two Red-faced Lovebirds and a Waxbill*, 1756.

OPPOSITE: Aert Schouman, *A Long-tailed Widowbird from Africa with a Blue-crowned Hanging Parrot from Asia*, 1783.

ABOVE: Aert Schouman, *Wild Fowl*, date unknown. Guineafowl from Africa with golden pheasant from China.

LEFT: Aert Schouman, *Two Rock-skimmers, Blue and Purple, on a Wall*, date unknown.

Chapter Four

BEFORE ECOLOGY

BEFORE ECOLOGY

Early natural history studies involved observing, note taking, collecting, naming, and describing. Some writing was more organized and focused than others, but few writers did any real analysis. Mostly, their work was just a compilation of notes and ideas jotted down after generally random observations. Science, conversely, is the systematic study of the natural world through planned observation and/or experimentation.

During the Age of Enlightenment (*c.*1715–89) in both Europe and America, natural history was focused on the identification of organisms. This meant that standards of practice had to become more consistent between continents. Conventions had to be established. Early American naturalists used European methodology, but Americans did more fieldwork and collected more specimens. Each supported the other.

As natural history became more thoughtful, detailed, and systematic, so did the art that accompanied it. Field observation became more reflective of reality. So did art. Most naturalists were not innate artists but took up art as a way to expand their study of nature. Conversely, when artists took an interest in nature, their skills gave bird art real authenticity.

Both Thomas Bewick and Alexander Wilson wrote the text for many of their illustrations, as their fieldwork gave them considerable experience in and knowledge of ornithology. Lady Gwillim's pencilled notes on her illustrations were not as formal but were just as informative. Bewick set his birds in a detailed landscape, while Gwillim's backgrounds were simpler. Wilson's paintings generally lacked much of a background, but he often showed some life history details such as a warbler feeding a young cowbird; the latter species is a brood parasite, which lays its eggs in the warbler's nest for the warbler to rear.

As more was learned about birds and their habitat, artists realized how important it was to show birds in the context of their environment. Simply placing them on a branch or a rock was not sufficient to explain where and how they lived. Naturalists were now studying the relationships of organisms to one another and their physical habitat. Ecology, from the Greek meaning "the study of home", slowly came into being. As true today as it was then, studies of birds are at the forefront of ecological discovery.

PREVIOUS PAGE: Alexander Wilson, *Blue Jay, Yellow Bird or Goldfinch, Baltimore Bird (Oriole)*, date unknown.

OPPOSITE: Thomas Bewick, *The Yellow Owl, Gillihowlet, Church, Barn, or Screech Owl*, from *A History of British Birds* (1797–1804).

ABOVE: Lady Elizabeth Symonds Gwillim, *Small Green-billed Malkoha*, 1801. This is a misidentification: it is actually a blue-faced malkoha. The damaged tail feathers indicate that this was a captive bird.

THOMAS BEWICK
English, 1753–1828

Born near Ovingham, Northumberland, Thomas Bewick was the oldest of eight children born to parents who were tenant farmers on eight acres of land leased for four pounds a year.

Although not excelling at schoolwork, Bewick displayed a talent for art, covering his school slate, and apparently his home's stone floor, with chalk sketches. He attended school until, at the age of 14, he took an apprenticeship with engraver Ralph Beilby. During his seven-year apprenticeship, he learned how to engrave on wood and metal and soon specialized in wood engraving. Years later, Bewick joined Beilby's business in Newcastle as a partner.

Before Bewick, printed works were illustrated with woodcuts. The early cutters used carpenter's tools that could produce fine details, but publishers began to prefer copper engraving, which gave a finer effect. Bewick pioneered the technique of "wood engraving". This involved using metal engraving tools to engrave blocks out of boxwood, a tree with a tight grain; unlike in traditional woodcuts, he cut across the grain, which made the blocks more durable.

Eventually Bewick began illustrating, writing, and publishing his own books. Bewick and Beilby had 30 apprentices working for them. In 1790 they published

OPPOSITE: Thomas Bewick, *The Black Woodpecker*, from *A History of British Birds* (1797–1804).

BELOW LEFT: Thomas Bewick, *Carrion Crow*, from *A History of British Birds*.

BELOW RIGHT: Thomas Bewick, *Pintail Duck* (now northern pintail), from *A History of British Birds*.

A General History of Quadrupeds, an illustrated work of over 500 pages. The book indicates that its interest is not in the classification of animals, but wishes "to give a clear and concise account of the nature, habits, and disposition of each, accompanied with more accurate representations" than have been published before. The publication was intended for children, but it was much admired by adults. So the author-illustrators embarked on a more serious work of natural history, *A History of British Birds*: the work for which Bewick is best known.

As he prepared this book, local people and seafarers sent him birds, both live and dead. These, along with his detailed observations in nature, animated his work. Bewick engraved wood blocks for the first volume, *Land Birds*, and gave the writing assignment to Beilby who struggled with it, so Bewick took on the authoring. As a result, Beilby's name did not appear on the title page when it was published in 1797. The resulting disagreement over that volume caused the partnership to dissolve. The next volume, *Water Birds,* published in 1804, was produced by Bewick with help from his apprentices. It was as successful as the first volume. Only the wealthy could afford natural history books produced with copper engravings, but Bewick's woodcuts were far less expensive and thus available to a larger segment of the population. Wood engravings were the ordinary man's art.

The book is organized into logical groups by feeding habits, such as granivorous (seed-eating), omnivorous, and carnivorous bird families. The common and scientific names are noted, as are the birds' behaviour, their physical features, and their distribution. Bewick's book is sometimes considered to be the first "field guide" for birdwatchers. The book was reprinted several times, with a sixth edition in 1826, a posthumous edition in 1832, and a memorial edition in 1885.

Bewick's wood engravings were accurate representations, engraved either from life or from skins, but many of the birds seem stiff, as if frightened. For example, the magpie, snipe, and thrush look as if they are braced for take-off.

A History of British Birds had some eminent admirers. J J Audubon (see page 86) first described the bird known as the Bewick's wren and named it after Bewick because "I enjoyed the pleasure of a personal acquaintance with him, and found him at all times a most agreeable, kind, and benevolent friend". *A History of British Birds* was a favourite of Charlotte Brontë's, and a short poem of William Wordsworth begins, "O that the genius of Bewick were mine".

LADY ELIZABETH SYMONDS GWILLIM
English, 1763–1807

Elizabeth Symonds Gwillim was born in Wye, Hereford, the daughter of a stonemason and architect. She married Henry Gwillim, a lawyer, at the age of 17 or 18, after which they, along with her sister Mary, moved to Madras (now Chennai), India.

While there, Elizabeth recorded in letters her life in India and painted both landscapes and the birds of the country, while Henry served as a judge in the colonial judiciary. The family became very involved in the social scene; however, although they enjoyed visiting and hosting fellow British visitors, they complained of a lack of privacy, so the sisters began to spend more time in the countryside. This gave them more opportunity for painting, Elizabeth focusing on birds while Mary painted fish and flowers.

OPPOSITE: Lady Elizabeth Symonds Gwillim, *Crested Honey Buzzard*, 1801.

Lady Gwillim's watercolours of Indian birds in their natural habitat were comparable to those of John James Audubon (see page 86) – who would not arrive on the art scene for another generation. In the early 1800s, ladies were expected to draw pretty pictures, but it was considered inappropriate for a woman to be a "real" artist. So, unlike Audubon, she never published her paintings – a total of 201 works, produced in less than six years in India.

Some of Lady Gwillim's paintings contained pencilled descriptions of the bird, with references to its habitat, natural history, differences in the sexes, and other information that indicated her knowledge of ornithology. In each case, the bird was placed in a suitable background, with the appropriate trees, shrubs, and other parts of the Indian landscape that the bird inhabited.

Her paintings are noteworthy not only because they were drawn from life but also because of their size. Almost all of the drawings are life-size. This is impressive because there are some very large birds in India. For example the grey heron picture measures 84 by 61 cm (33 by 24 inches); the bird itself, with an outstretched neck, measures 1 metre (39 inches) tall. The 81 cm/32 inch-tall Eurasian bittern is painted 76 cm (30 inches) tall. Even the largest vultures are painted at life size. Audubon produced the first full-length portraits of birds, but when original paintings are compared, Lady Gwillim takes the prize. Her faithful representation of living birds attests to both her skills as an artist and her acute observation of nature. Terrance Michael Short, former ornithologist at the Royal Ontario Museum where her paintings reside, noted that her portraits are among "the finest ever done of Asian birds".

Buteo ... huparcilis

Indian Crested Honey-Buzzard [K.B. #278]

Pond Heron or Paddy Bird
(*Ardeola grayii*)

ABOVE: Lady Elizabeth Symonds Gwillim, *Indian Pond Heron*, 1801.

OPPOSITE: Lady Elizabeth Symonds Gwillim, *Eurasian Bittern*, 1801.

Lady Gwillim died on 21 December 1807 of unknown causes and was buried at St Mary's Church in Madras; her husband later returned to England with the paintings.

In the late eighteenth century, under colonial rule, the British wanted to record their life in India and hired Indian artists to do so. Wanting to capture everyday scenes, realism became an important focus of Indian art and Lady Gwillim may have had some influence.

ABOVE: Lady Elizabeth
Symonds Gwillim,
Common Iora, 1801.

OPPOSITE: Lady
Elizabeth Symonds
Gwillim, *Bronze-winged
Jacana*, 1801.

BEFORE ECOLOGY

Jacana (Metopidius indicus).

WILD TURKEY. *Meleagris Gallopavo.* 1 Male. 2 Female. 3 Young.

ALEXANDER WILSON

Scottish, 1766–1813

The man who came to be known as the "father of American ornithology", Alexander Wilson, was born in Paisley, Scotland. At the age of 10 or 11 years, he began an apprenticeship as a weaver. Five years later, he left home and began to wander the countryside, working when he had to, and writing poetry.

Some of Wilson's poems were political satire aimed at the mills where weavers worked. After he was imprisoned for his words, he decided to try his luck elsewhere.

At the age of 27, with a nephew, he boarded a ship for a four-month journey to Delaware on the east coast of the United States, sleeping on the deck the entire way. After his arrival he worked as a labourer, printer, and weaver but then moved to New Jersey and then to Gray's Ferry, Pennsylvania, where he began a career as a teacher. While there he met Alexander Lawson, another Scot, who taught him drawing, painting, and etching, and William Bartram, the first naturalist to explore the dense tropical forests of Florida. Bartram was one of the first naturalists to compile a bird list of the United States, with 215 specimens. He encouraged Wilson's talent in painting and interest in nature, especially ornithology. Wilson used Bartram's library and sent him many of his drawings for his opinion.

Around 1803 Wilson began a series of wanderings that included walking from Gray's Ferry to Niagara Falls, over 640 km (400 miles), watching birds along the way. He studied art and ornithology en route. In 1806 he became the assistant editor of the American edition of *Rees's Cyclopedia*, an important nineteenth-century British encyclopedia. This gave him the opportunity and time to pursue his dream of publishing a colour book of all the birds in America; this became his famous work *American Ornithology*. The *Cyclopedia* publisher, Samuel Bradford, was impressed with Wilson's diligence and skills and financially backed Wilson's work, on the condition that Wilson find 200 subscribers – interested parties who would promise to buy the book. Wilson kept travelling, typically alone, selling subscriptions, collecting information, and working on his drawings. In seven years he travelled more than 19,300 km (12,000 miles), mostly on foot.

Unusually for the time, Wilson wrote most of the text for the drawings. He had no formal training as an artist, writer, or scientist, and owned few books, but his writing indicates that he was a keen natural historian and recorded his observations closely. *Volume I*, with two to six birds on each of ten plates, appeared in 1808. He ultimately published nine volumes of *American Ornithology*, from 1808 to 1814.

OPPOSITE: Alexander Wilson, *Wild Turkey*, from *American Ornithology* (1808).

Drawn from Nature by A. Wilson   1. Virginian Rail.   2. Clapper R.   3. Blue Crane.   4. Little Egret.   Engraved by I.G. Warnicke

ABOVE: Alexander Wilson, *Wading Birds*, from *American Ornithology*. Shows a Virginian (Virginia) rail, clapper rail, blue crane (little blue heron), and little snowy egret.

OPPOSITE: Alexander Wilson, *Red-winged Starling* (actually blackbird), *c.*1808–1814.

Wilson spent a considerable amount of his time selling subscriptions to the nine volumes, at $120 each – more than he made as a teacher in a year. He spent six months travelling by rowing boat and on horseback, some 4,820 km (3,000 miles), collecting bird specimens and selling subscriptions. He garnered 250 subscribers, making his first delivery to the White House and Thomas Jefferson.

According to Audubon, Wilson tried to sell a subscription to Audubon, a shopkeeper in Kentucky at the time, but became depressed when Audubon (see page 86) showed Wilson his own collection of bird drawings. Wilson did not mention this meeting in his letters, so the story is questionable.

American Ornithology contained illustrations and descriptions of 268 species of birds, 26 of them previously unknown. Wilson's drawings are excellent, but he focused on the external anatomy of the birds rather than behaviour or habitat. His drawings are the precursors of the drawings we find in today's field guides, showing the characteristics and poses by which one would identify a bird. Many of the western birds in his book he never saw but drew from specimens collected by others, including the famous US explorers Meriwether Lewis and William Clark. One painting of three birds includes Clark's nutcracker, Lewis's woodpecker, and the western tanager, birds that he probably never saw alive.

Unfortunately, Wilson died of dysentery before the completion of the work; the book was finished by George Ord, an American ornithologist and writer.

Drawn from Nature by A. Wilson 30 *Engraved by A. Lawson*

1. Red-winged Starling. 2. Female. 3. Black-poll Warbler. 4. Lesser Red-poll.

ABOVE: John James Audubon, *Wilson's Storm Petrel*, from *Birds of America*, original double elephant folio (1827–30). This is one of five species of birds named after Alexander Wilson.

OPPOSITE: Alexander Wilson, *Quails*, date unknown. A pair of California quails are shown at the bottom and an immature bird at the top.

The scientist and historian Elliot Coues noted that, "Perhaps no work on ornithology of equal extent is equally free from error". He goes on to say "Science would lose little if every scrap of pre-Wilsonian writing about United States birds could be annihilated". Higher praise can hardly be imagined.

Wilson so impressed the ornithological world with his work that several birds were named after him: Wilson's warbler, Wilson's snipe, Wilson's storm petrel, Wilson's phalarope, and Wilson's plover. The Wilson Ornithological Society, founded in 1888, is a major scientific ornithological association in the United States, publishing the *Wilson Journal of Ornithology*.

Chapter Five

EARLY SCIENTIFIC ILLUSTRATION

PREVIOUS PAGE: J J Audubon,
*American (now Greater)
Flamingo,* from *Birds of
America* (1838).

ABOVE: John and Elizabeth
Gould, *Major Mitchell's
Cockatoo,* from the Goulds'
The Birds of Australia
(1840–48).

OPPOSITE: J J Audubon, *Wild
Turkey,* from *Birds of America.*

I llustration is art that strives to put across information or ideas. It may be
accompanied by wording or it may just consist of visual images. Posters,
flyers, billboards, textbooks, and other media use illustrations to clarify the
information that they convey. Scientific illustrations are no different, except
that they are aimed at a smaller audience and the emphasis is on accuracy
and usefulness rather than aesthetics (although much scientific illustration is
attractive as well).

For hundreds of years, scientific illustration was focused on natural sciences
and on entire organisms. The earliest natural historians sketched their
observations, although some turned out to be flights of fancy. Conrad Gessner
in his *Historia Animalium* of 1604 depicts a goat-mermaid he called a "sea-devil".
"Bestiaries" were illustrated volumes that described various animals, each usually
accompanied by a moral lesson. No distinction was made between existing and
mythical birds, so the phoenix was mentioned along with the pelican. Eventually,
most of these imaginary creatures disappeared from serious texts.

As ornithologists and artists paid closer attention to birds, they noticed more
subtle characteristics, such as the shape of birds' feet: were they webbed, lobed, or
fitted with long talons? Are their bills straight, thin, wide, upcurved, or hooked?
What are the identifying characteristics – wing bars, eye rings, fancy plumes, or
iridescent colours? The more they observed, the more they learned, and the more
detail went into their artwork.

Most of a bird's exterior is feathers. Illustrating feather texture is a challenge,
but even more so is the accurate depiction of the shapes of particular feathers.
The primary (outer) feathers of the wing are asymmetrical but increasingly
less so towards the middle, transitioning to the inner, more symmetrical,
secondary feathers. Spread wings reflect the aerodynamic properties of the bird.
The feathers on the thumb serve as a flap to reduce turbulence and need to be
properly depicted during take-off and landing; the same applies to tail feathers.
The wings and the body are covered with overlapping feathers called coverts that
streamline the body for smooth airflow. Precise drawing is needed for an accurate
illustration.

As we progress through the ages by briefly discussing artists of the time, the
depiction of birds, both through the artists' skills and the new tools available to
them, is evolving.

PLATE 1

Wild Turkey. MELEAGRIS GALLOPAVO, Linn.   *Male.* American Cane. *Miegia macrosperma.*

Drawn from nature by J.J.Audubon F.R.S.F.L.S.   Engraved by W.H.Lizars Edin.
Retouched by R.Havell Junr.

The Mocking Bird, 1 Male. 2 F.

TURDUS POLYGLOTTUS.

Plant Vulge. Yellow Jessamin.

Drawn from Nature and Published by John J. Audubon, F.R.S.E. M.W.S.

Rattlesnake.

CROTALUS HORRIDUS.

Engraved, Printed and Coloured by R. Havell & Son, London.

JOHN JAMES AUDUBON
French-Haitian, 1785–1851

On being asked to name a bird artist, most people might struggle to name anyone besides Audubon. J J Audubon's colour plate book, Birds of America *(1838), is one of the finest books ever produced in the field of ornithology.*

Audubon was born in what is now Haiti, but political unrest convinced the family to move to France. At 18, Jean-Jacques Fougère Audubon immigrated to the United States and changed his name to John James Audubon.

Audubon made his way to rural Pennsylvania, where he wandered around the forested hills. He hunted, observed, collected, and sketched, developing a fascination for wildlife; his interest in both birds and art developed exponentially.

He married a neighbour, moved to Kentucky and opened a dry goods store. While Audubon was running the store, Alexander Wilson (see page 76) stopped by, trying to sell a subscription to his *American Ornithology*. Audubon's assistant whispered in French to him that his (Audubon's) drawings were better than those of Wilson; Audubon refused to buy. With the store failing, he moved to Ohio and then Louisiana. Financially unsuccessful, he filed for bankruptcy in 1819. After some jail time for his financial failures, Audubon supported himself, just barely, by doing chalk drawings of people he met and teaching French. He ultimately decided that he would find and paint every bird in America, beginning by observing and drawing birds he observed along the Mississippi River. Supported by his wife's salary as a teacher, Audubon created a large portfolio of drawings and paintings by 1826 and sailed to England to find a publisher; his work was enthusiastically received in Britain, and this enabled him to publish the first illustrations.

Audubon's *Birds of America* showed birds in realistic situations, such as the mockingbird nest being attacked by a snake. Audubon was also a storyteller and (with Scottish ornithologist William MacGillivray) wrote *Ornithological Biographies* to accompany the pictures. He shot birds in order to study them close up, as others did before and after him. But to depict birds in lifelike poses he created armatures of wire and wood on which he mounted the dead birds. Observation in the field allowed him to create realistic poses, often portraying them in action. He painted birds life-size, but sometimes, as in the *Great Blue Heron* painting, he had to put the neck of the 106 cm/42 inch-tall bird in an awkward position to fit it all on the 99 cm/39 inch paper, the largest paper size available for printing in the early nineteenth century.

OPPOSITE: J J Audubon, *Mocking Birds and Rattlesnake*, from *Birds of America* (1838).

ABOVE: J J Audubon, *Eastern Phoebe* (the birds Audubon banded), from *Birds of America*.

PLATE. CCXI.

Great blue Heron. ARDEA HERODIAN. Male.

Done in watercolour, the originals were transferred to copper engravings and printed, mostly in black and white. Then each was hand-painted by an assembly line of colourists, perhaps as many as 150. There are 435 plates showing 1,055 birds.

Audubon sold subscriptions for *Birds of America*, issued in 87 parts between 1827 and 1838. Every few months, subscribers would receive a package of five prints: a large bird, a medium-sized bird, and three smaller ones. The complete set cost subscribers $1,000. Audubon made a decent living, settled in New York City, and continued to travel in quest of more birds. In 1841 an edition one-eighth the size of the original, an "octavo", was published; this made the work less expensive and very popular. At 25 by 15 cm (10 by 6 inches), it was a little bigger than most of today's field guides, but it was the first bird identification book that was accessible to the average person.

There has been controversy over the years regarding certain of Audubon's paintings, which resemble the work of Alexander Wilson. Audubon's *Bald Eagle*, *Mississippi Kite*, and *Red-winged Blackbirds* so resemble those of Wilson that it is hard to imagine this being a coincidence.

Whatever the case, Audubon introduced ornithological art to the public as no one else ever had. And even though he shot hundreds of birds, and ate many of them, his name is now synonymous with bird conservation. The Audubon Society was founded in his name in 1886, in response to the slaughter of birds to make fashion accessories. And he was one of only two Americans to be elected Fellows of the Royal Society of London, the foremost scientific organization of the time; the other was Benjamin Franklin.

Named after Audubon are Audubon's Oriole, Audubon's Shearwater, and a species of warbler formerly known as Audubon's.

ABOVE: J J Audubon, *Immature Bald Eagle*, from *Birds of America*.

OPPOSITE: J J Audubon, *Great Blue Heron*, from *Birds of America*. The bird's neck is bent in an awkward position in order to fit the entire 106 cm/42 inch bird onto the 91 cm/36 inch paper.

OPPOSITE: J J Audubon,
American White Pelican, from
Birds of America.

RIGHT: J J Audubon, *Snowy Owl*,
from *Birds of America*.

PRIDEAUX JOHN SELBY
English, 1788–1867

ABOVE: Prideaux John Selby, *Great Bustard*, from *Illustrations of British Ornithology* (1821–34).

OPPOSITE: Prideaux John Selby, *Hen Harrier, Male and Female*, from *Illustrations of British Ornithology*.

Selby is best known for his Illustrations of British Ornithology *(1821–34), the first set of life-size illustrations of British birds. In Selby's work we find scientific information and organization that Audubon and others neglected, such as different plumages, male and female, immature and mature, and winter and spring.*

Selby recognizes those distinctions; Audubon may not have done so. Audubon's "Selby's warbler", or flycatcher, is actually a female hooded warbler, for example, and his "Washington's eagle" was probably an immature bald eagle. Selby also includes a glossary of technical terms, mostly anatomical, and organizes species by taxon and scientific name. This was an advance in the natural sciences – recognizing the relationships of birds in a systematic manner.

Selby was born in Northumberland, England at his family's estate, Twizell House, his father the head of an old and influential family. As a boy, Selby studied the habits of local birds, drew them, and learned how to preserve and display specimens from the family butler, a skilled taxidermist. By 12 or 13 years of age Selby had written a manuscript noting the habits of some common birds, illustrated with attractive colour drawings. After some time at University College, Oxford, he dropped out and went home to attend to his estate when his father died in 1804.

Selby became a gentleman naturalist with a passion for natural history, especially ornithology, and whose abilities as an artist and intellectual made him a major figure in the British scientific community. In 1819, Selby aimed to create a set of life-size illustrations of every bird in Britain. Selby drew birds, assisted by his brother-in-law, Robert Mitford, but because neither knew how to engrave plates, Mitford travelled to Newcastle, where he was taught by Thomas Bewick. In turn, Mitford taught Selby. William Home Lizars, an outstanding engraver who produced many plates for major natural history publications of the time, helped to refine some of Selby's engravings.

Twizell House became a stopping point for naturalists travelling from London to Edinburgh. Audubon visited in 1827, selling subscriptions to his *Birds of America*; he and Selby became good friends. Audubon drew a lapwing for Selby as a gift, and Selby's later painting of a green lapwing has an Audubon-like appearance. Apparently, Selby also took some painting lessons from Audubon.

Selby's elephant-size *Illustrations of British Ornithology*, in 19 parts, consists of two large folios: one on land birds, published in 1825, and one on water birds,

PLATE X.

HEN HARRIER.
1. Male.
2. Female.

WHITE SPOONBILL. MALE.

published in 1833, sold by subscription for £105. It took Selby 14 years to complete the project. The work consisted of 218 plates depicting 280 species of birds plus four anatomy plates, but no text. Most birds were shown one to a plate, with excellent rendering of details but little or no background. Selby organized the birds systematically and included a glossary of anatomical terms used to describe the detailed features of various birds. That was another major step in the development of natural history as a science.

Life-size, Selby's bird figures were considered the finest and most realistic of any British birds done to date. Perhaps the only reason Selby did not get as much recognition as he probably deserves is because of John and Elizabeth Gould's *Birds of Europe*, published at about the same time. The Goulds' work contained many of the same species as Selby's and was produced with lithography, a more modern technique that attracted popular attention.

ABOVE: Prideaux John Selby, *Eurasian Spoonbill*, from *Illustrations of British Ornithology*.

LEFT: Prideaux John Selby, *Fork-tailed Flycatcher*, from *Illustrations of British Ornithology*.

OPPOSITE: Prideaux John Selby, *Great-eared Owl*, from *Illustrations of British Ornithology*.

GREAT EARED OWL. 21.

ELIZABETH GOULD

English, 1804–41

Elizabeth Albin (1708–41) was perhaps the first woman to illustrate bird books, but she was followed by another woman who became better known. Elizabeth Gould (née Coxen) was a prolific artist, producing many illustrations for ornithological works, including some in Charles Darwin's The Zoology of the Voyage of H.M.S. Beagle.

Typical of young ladies of her class in pre-Victorian times, she was taught music, dancing, modern languages, drawing, and painting – skills intended to make her an accomplished woman. At the age of 22, Elizabeth became governess to an aristocrat, but she found the position dull. She married John Gould, ornithologist and taxidermist, when both were 24.

John Gould established a taxidermy business in London in 1824 and later worked for the Zoological Society of London. There he met the leading naturalists of England and was often the first to see avian specimens given to the Society. John began writing ornithological works, and Elizabeth created drawings to accompany John's letters to colleagues. Elizabeth also learned lithography from Edward Lear, an English artist, musician, and author, so that she could create illustrations for John's work. (Lithography, a printing technique invented in 1796, involved drawing with carbon and crayon on a smooth block of stone, and produced a softer image than wood or metal engraving. The technique rapidly became popular and would slowly replace engraving over the next 50 years.)

In 1830 John Gould decided to publish a volume of hand-painted lithographs of rare Indian birds to sell by subscription. Elizabeth produced 80 lithographs, based on her drawings of taxidermy specimens and representing about a hundred species of birds, many of which were previously unknown to science. This effort became the highly successful work *A Century of Birds from the Himalaya Mountains.* ("*Century*" in the title refers to the 102 birds illustrated.)

The Goulds then began another project, *The Birds of Europe.* Over five years, Elizabeth produced 380 out of 448 plates, the remainder being made by Edward Lear. While the birds of India were stuffed and mounted and appeared stiff, many of the birds of Europe were drawn while alive, although caged. This made Elizabeth's drawings more realistic and the colours more real, because the soft parts of birds, such as the eyes, wattles, and skin of the legs and feet, fade in death. She also introduced natural backgrounds to the drawings. Elizabeth's technique advanced rapidly as she added depth, motion, and character, and she became known for producing beautiful, accurate works.

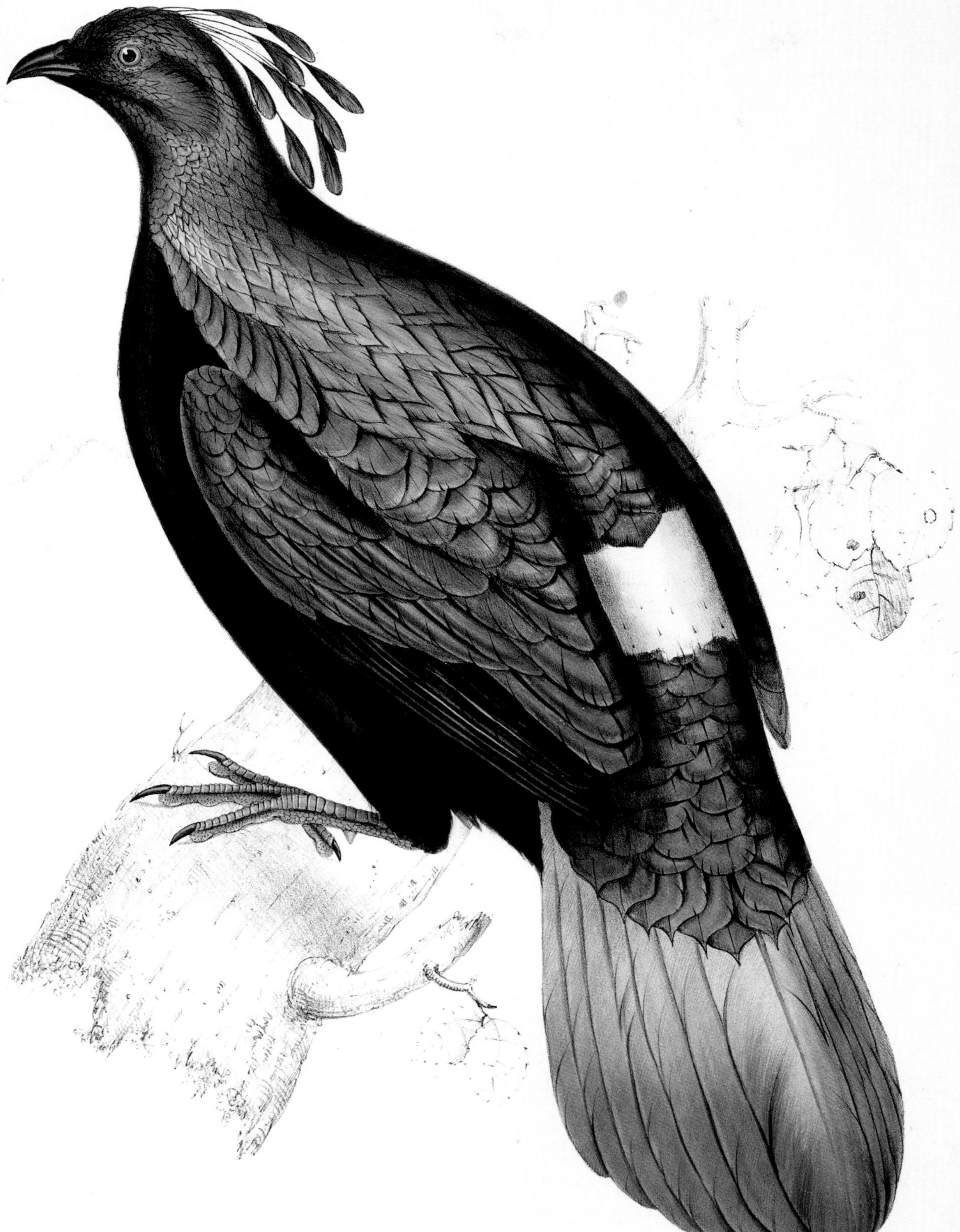

PTILONORHYNCHUS HOLOSERICEUS. *Kuhl*

ABOVE: Elizabeth Gould, *Satin Bowerbird*, from John and Elizabeth Gould's *The Birds of Australia* (1840–48).

OPPOSITE: John and Elizabeth Gould, *Trogon ardens* (now *Harpactes ardens*, Philippine Trogon), from John Gould's *A Monograph of the Trogonidae, or Family of Trogons* (1838).

From 1835 to 1838, the Goulds published *A Monograph of the Trogonidae, or Family of Trogons*. John and Elizabeth's names are on all 36 plates, but Lear produced some of the backgrounds. Between 1858 and 1875 a second edition of the Trogon book was published. Many new species had been discovered as expeditions moved deeper into the tropical forest. The new edition added 36 more plates, and the previous plates were redrawn, showing birds in motion and adding more background, including fruits and flowers – a reflection of the new information learned about trogons and their habitat.

The most ambitious and well known of the Goulds' projects is *The Birds of Australia*. They travelled to the country in 1838, leaving their three youngest children in England. As was typical then, explorers and naturalists shot their objects of study. John was an avid collector, described by Elizabeth as "a great enemy to the feathered tribe". Working from dead specimens as well as caged ones, Elizabeth honed her skill, which reached a pinnacle with magnificent plates of the satin bowerbird, superb fairy-wren (called the blue warbler then), and various parrot species. The seven-volume *The Birds of Australia* continues to be the classic work on the subject.

100.

PTILORIS PARADISEA: *Swains*:

J. Gould and HC Richter del et lith.

Hullmandel & Walt

ABOVE: John and Elizabeth Gould, *Geospiza magnirostris* (large ground finch), from Charles Robert Darwin's *The Zoology of the Voyage of the HMS Beagle, Part III: Birds* (1838–41).

OPPOSITE: Elizabeth Gould, *Ptiloris paradiseus* (paradise riflebird), from *The Birds of Australia*.

Exhibiting superb detail in her drawings, Elizabeth Gould was one of the first scientific illustrators. She meets the standards of today's Guild of Natural Science Illustrators: the depictions have to appeal to the eye, and the work must include the correct proportions and anatomical structures.

In 1841, shortly after the birth of her eighth child, Elizabeth Gould died, only eleven years after she began her career in avian art. There is considerable discussion in the literature concerning John Gould's failure to fully credit her for her work, often taking the credit himself for designs that she created and he merely altered or approved. Sometimes she was just ignored. The plates of the Galapagos finches, which Darwin discussed in his *On the Origin of Species*, do not bear her name. However, two bird species – the Gouldian finch and Mrs Gould's sunbird – were named after her.

Chapter Six

IN THE AGE OF DARWIN

Charles Darwin made his famous voyage on HMS *Beagle* from 1831 to 1836. By the time he returned to England he had established his reputation as a scientist. He went on to publish his notes on the *Beagle* survey and eventually his classic 1859 book *On the Origin of Species*. By the 1870s the theories of natural selection and evolution were well accepted by the scientific community.

Before Darwin there had been many ideas as to how animals and plants came to be. Aristotle hinted at the concept in his Great Chain of Being, in which each species was created individually and belonged in a hierarchy of usefulness in nature. Abbé Pluche, a French priest, published *Spectacle de la Nature* (1732–42), noting that birds' bodies are shaped by their habits: for example, a heron's neck is long because it reaches for fish. Lamarck's similar 1801 theory of inheritance of acquired characteristics proposed the same idea but in a more scientific fashion. In the mid-eighteenth century Georges-Louis Leclerc, Comte de Buffon, considered that similar forms might have arisen from a common ancestor. And there were other thoughts, many consistent with religious beliefs in that a superior being created organisms just the way they are. Today's term for that idea is creationism or intelligent design.

Carl Linnaeus's 1735 *Systema Naturae* outlined ideas for the hierarchical classification of organisms. By the end of the nineteenth century his system of binomial classification had become the standard. Old ideas hung on, but as artists and scientists began to work more closely together, artwork became more reflective of scientists' work.

How much Darwin influenced the artists he worked with and how much the artists influenced him is debatable, but considering Darwin's experience and the reams of data he collected, it is unlikely that artists had much of an effect on his thoughts. But perhaps the drawings he saw, depicting poses, movement, and colour, made him think about how certain features arose. Darwin checked out books illustrated by Edward Lear from the Royal Society Library and called one of Lear's books "a great work".

Darwin's finches of the Galapagos are the most famous examples of evolution, but there were more. He showed a considerable interest in the process of sexual selection in birds in which one sex, usually the male, dons an attractive plumage to attract a mate. Presumably, Darwin would have been curious about showy, colourful birds such as parrots or peacocks, common art subjects of his time.

PREVIOUS PAGE: Edward Lear, *Yellow-bibbed Lory*, from *Illustrations of the Family of Psittacidae, or Parrots* (1832).

OPPOSITE: Edward Lear, *Scarlet Macaw*, 1830. An early parrot painting.

MACROCERCUS ARACANGA.

Red and Yellow Maccaw.

2/3 Nat. Size.

EDWARD LEAR
English, 1812–88

Lear was an English artist, illustrator, musician, author, and poet, known mostly today for nonsense poems and prose and especially his limericks, a form of poetry that he made popular.

Edward Lear was born in London, the twentieth of 21 children. His father was a stockbroker, but money problems broke the family up, and the children were dispersed to various households. Lear went to live with his sister, 21 years older, who ended up mothering him until he was 50 years old, partly because he suffered from epilepsy, bronchitis, and asthma. She taught him to write and encouraged his interest in drawing. He began by copying drawings, including every plate in the Comte de Buffon's 44-volume *Histoire Naturelle*. By the age of 16 he had begun work as a draughtsman, drawing animals for the Zoological Society – employment that he took to earn his "bread and cheese". Lear made drawings in colour and later contributed to the illustrations of poems by Alfred, Lord Tennyson.

Lear began painting parrots in 1830 at the age of 18, using birds at the London Zoological Society as models, with the aim of drawing all members of the parrot family and publishing the work by subscription in 14 folios. Two years later he had published 42 parrot paintings entitled *Illustrations of the Family of Psittacidae*. The paintings were remarkable, capturing accurately the poses of the birds and their feather texture. The day after the book's publication, the teenaged Lear was nominated as an Associate of the Linnean Society.

Although the parrot book was artistically excellent, it failed financially and was never completed. He printed 175 copies, not enough to pay his expenses, and sold only 125; even then payments were often late or lacking. And he completed only 42 of a planned 50 lithographs. But the work made him famous; Lear gained the reputation as one of the best natural history artists of the time. He even gave a young Queen Victoria drawing lessons.

In 1831 Lear published his first drawing, a great auk from a specimen in the British Museum, for Prideaux John Selby's *Illustrations of British Ornithology* (see page 92). From 1832 to 1836 Lear worked for Edward Stanley, the 13th Earl of Derby and President of the Linnean Society, drawing birds in Stanley's private menagerie.

Lear was the first major bird artist to draw birds from life instead of skins, although less renowned artists had done so for years. At the time most bird illustrators hired engravers to reproduce their work, but Lear did not have the financial wherewithal to hire a skilled craftsman. Engraving plates not only meant paying someone, but also meant that someone else redid your work, possibly compromising it. Lear created his art using lithography, so all his work was entirely his own. Lithography was a new and detailed process that required

There was an Old Man with a beard, who said, "It is just as I feared!—
Two Owls and a Hen, four Larks and a Wren,
Have all built their nests in my beard!"

ABOVE: Edward Lear, "There was an Old Man with a beard, who said, 'It is just as I feared! Two Owls and a Hen, four Larks and a Wren, Have all built their nests in my beard!'", from *A Book of Nonsense* (c.1875).

OPPOSITE: Edward Lear, *Kuhl's Parakeet*, from *Illustrations of the Family of Psittacidae, or Parrots* (1832).

SNOWY OWL.
Surix Nyctea *(Linn)*

ABOVE: Edward Lear, *Purple Heron*, from John and Elizabeth Gould's *The Birds of Europe* (1832–37).

ABOVE RIGHT: Edward Lear, *Snowy Owl*, from *The Birds of Europe*. Lithographed by Edward Lear.

OPPOSITE: Edward Lear, *Lord Derby's Parakeet (Psittacula derbiana)*, 1831. Also known as Derbyan parakeet, the name commemorates Edward Stanley, 13th Earl of Derby.

several steps. Lear captioned an early draft of the purple-naped lory "my first lithographic failure".

Lear then began employment with John and Elizabeth Gould (see page 96), drawing backgrounds for their first book, *A Century of Birds from the Himalayan Mountains*. Later, Lear and the Goulds visited zoos and collections in various parts of Europe, eventually producing 448 plates of *The Birds of Europe*, 68 of which were drawn by Lear. He also assisted Elizabeth with *The Family of Trogons* and taught her lithography. However, the Goulds never acknowledged his contribution. He drew 10 plates of the Goulds' *Family of Toucans*, but his signature was erased from the plates in the second edition. After John Gould's death in 1881, Lear wrote: "He was one I never liked really".

Lear's eyesight began to decline, prompting him to say, "no birds under an ostrich should I soon be able to see to do". In 1835, he changed his artistic focus to travel and landscape painting.

Lear probably contributed illustrations to Darwin's *Voyage of the Beagle* journal of 1839, and Darwin was known to consult Lear's scientific illustrations in the 1840s and 1850s. Lear's macaw, an endangered species from Brazil, was named in his honour.

In December of 1871 Lear published his new book of nonsense, which contained twice as many bird limericks as his first book.

Palæornis Derbyanus. Gray 1856.   *India.*

J.Wolf & J.Smit del et lith.

M.& N.Hanhart, imp.

CERIORNIS MELANOCEPHALA.

JOSEPH WOLF
German, 1820–99

Born in Prussia, Wolf carefully studied animals as a young man and demonstrated an innate ability to draw them. As a boy he would cut out paper silhouettes of birds and other animals and paste them onto windows in his village; the villagers saw his obsession with wildlife as odd.

After spending three years as an apprentice lithographer, Wolf went to Frankfurt at the age of 19 and introduced himself to Eduard Rüppell, an ornithologist at the Frankfurt Museum working on the birds of Abyssinia. Rüppell hired him to work on *The Birds of North-East Africa*, and also introduced him to another naturalist, Jakob Kaup. As well as employing him, Kaup in turn introduced Wolf to the head of the Natural History Museum in Leiden in the Netherlands, Professor Hermann Schlegel, who commissioned him to work on some plates for *Traité de Fauconnerie*, a set of life-size paintings of birds of prey and the history and techniques of falconry. Wolf attended art school in Leiden and learned oil painting and the development of background. He also painted the first 20 plates showing the birds of Japan, part of *Fauna Japonica*, the first serious descriptions of birds in that country. Schlegel said that he "was astounded at the accuracy of the attitudes…" and that "Wolf excelled any other natural history painter" that he had known.

In 1848 Wolf moved to London and worked on George Edward Gray's *The Genera of Birds*. Gray, curator of the British Museum's bird collection from 1831 until 1871, described more than 8,000 species, probably all the known species at that time. The artwork was done by Wolf, Edward Lear (see page 106), and others. In bird books like this in the nineteenth century, the emphasis was typically placed on the coloured plates, but especially noteworthy were Wolf's depictions of 345 heads.

John Gould hired Wolf and took him on a collecting trip to Norway. Wolf painted 79 plates for Gould for the *Birds of Great Britain* and *Birds of Asia*. Wolf also did some freelance work and became the illustrator of first choice for explorers and adventurers such as David Livingstone, Alfred Russel Wallace, and Henry Walter Bates. Charles Darwin, working on his study of animal expressions, asked Wolf to make some illustrations from photographs and living animals. Wolf did not agree with Darwin's interpretations of expressions, but they liked each other and Darwin often visited Wolf at home.

Wolf claimed that he was one of the few artists who could portray the textures and placement of feathers accurately. Perhaps this was an exaggeration, but he was good at depicting feathers, whether attached to the bird, floating through the air, or fallen to the ground.

TOP: Joseph Wolf, *Pacific Marsh Harrier*, from H Schlegel and A H Verster van Wulverhorst's *Traité de Fauconnerie* (1844). Once named *Circus wolfi, Circus approximans* is the official name.

ABOVE: Joseph Wolf, *Peacock*, from Daniel Girard Elliot's *A Monograph of the Phasianidae, or Family of the Pheasants* (1870–72).

OPPOSITE: Joseph Wolf, *Crimson-bellied Tragopan*, c.1870

Along with Dutch illustrator Joseph Smit, Wolf illustrated Daniel Girard Elliot's *A Monograph of the Phasianidae* (family of pheasants). Girard was a wealthy American zoologist, founder and president of the American Ornithologists' Union, and a founder of the American Museum of Natural History in New York.

Wolf's field observations of living birds made his illustrations, whether in oil, watercolour, woodcuts, or lithography very lifelike. He could produce accurate illustrations from memory. He was especially adept at painting birds with brown or grey plumage and making them as appealing as birds with brightly coloured plumage. Alfred Newton, an accomplished ornithologist at Cambridge, called Wolf "the greatest of all animal painters".

Joseph Wolf was the first important bird artist to publish works in scientific journals. The *Proceedings of the Zoological Society of London* contains over 300 paintings from his lithographs. From 1859, when the journal was initiated, until 1948, the British Ornithological Journal *Ibis* had a Black-headed Ibis on its cover, from a woodcut by Wolf. It was removed only after the woodcut wore down.

WILLIAM MATTHEW HART
Irish, 1830–1908

William Matthew Hart is not well known even though he drew birds for John Gould. Born in Limerick, Ireland, he originally planned to pursue medicine, but he did not have the financial resources to support that educational aim.

ABOVE: William Matthew Hart, *Cardinals*, from Volume 12 of *The Catalogue of Birds in the British Museum* (1888).

OPPOSITE: William Matthew Hart, *The Tooth-billed Hummingbird*, 1902.

Interested in natural history, as many men in medicine were in the nineteenth century, Hart managed to accumulate a large number of various medical and natural history items, particularly moths and butterflies. Early on he learned watercolour techniques, as his father was also an artist.

In 1851, Hart moved to London and began to work for Gould, beginning by colouring the lithographic plates and later drawing the "patterns" (master illustrations to be copied by the colourers) for the plates for a *Monograph of the Trochilidae, or Family of Hummingbirds*. Gould had never seen a hummingbird in the wild, but he had collected thousands of specimens for him and his colourers to work from.

Hart especially liked working with bright colours and created the metallic highlights of the lithographic plates. Gould made the rough sketches and Hart, along with Elizabeth Gould (see page 96), Henry Richter, and Joseph Wolf (see page 110), painted the finished drawings. Hart also worked on Gould's *Birds of Great Britain*, issued in 25 parts from 1862 to 1873, with Richter. Both of them prepared watercolours of the birds that were then transferred onto the lithographic stones.

By 1870 Hart was Gould's main artist and lithographer. *The Birds of New Guinea* was begun in 1871, and Hart lithographed 141 of Gould's sketches. The work was only half-finished when Gould died in 1873, but this project showed some of Hart's best work, the birds of paradise, because of the bright colours he was able to put to use. For example, on one plate two Raggiana Birds of Paradise face each other – one showing bright red flanks, the other yellow. The Blue Bird of Paradise painting is spectacular, but, working only from dead specimens, Hart did not realize that the male bird actually hangs upside down in its courtship display, as Darwin noted later.

Both Gould and Hart enjoyed fishing, and Gould was the proud owner of a painting by Hart of a trout that Gould caught in the Thames. As Edward Lear (see page 106) and others have noted, Gould was not one to give credit to his employees or co-workers. Hart was not given full credit for his work until he was employed by Richard Bowdler Sharpe, head of the bird collection at the British Museum of Natural History, on supplements of *The Birds of New Guinea* which were published after Gould's death. Gould did recognize Hart in his will, although he apparently did not know his first name as the will stated, "I give to my artist – Hart the sum of £250".

ABOVE: William Matthew Hart, *Pair of Barred Cuckooshrikes,* date unknown. Found in eastern Australia, Indonesia, Papua New Guinea, and the Solomon Islands.

OPPOSITE: William Matthew Hart, *Bolivian Warbling Finch,* 1888.

Hart also painted for a major work of Sharpe's: *Catalogue of the Birds in the British Museum*. He illustrated Volume 12, the other volumes being illustrated by Sharpe, John Gerrard Keulemans, Smit and others. Hart's plate showing the cardinals is especially attractive. In total, Hart either coloured, drew or lithographed more than 2,000 plates for a variety of bird books by different authors.

Chapter Seven

ART AND SCIENCE OVERLAP

As exploration of the natural world expanded, artists were there to record it. Photography emerged in the mid-nineteenth century, but until about 1920, shutter speeds were so slow that outdoor photography was not feasible, so scientists, who needed to authenticate their work with details, continued to rely on artists for accurate representations of nature.

Field observation was becoming more exhaustive, and the knowledge of birds' relationship to the environment and to each other became more important. Thousands of bird illustrations had been created by the twentieth century, but many were of little or no scientific value because they were more artistic than accurate. Audubon's paintings were spectacular, but they were portraiture, lending little to the knowledge of ornithology, although Audubon himself was a decent ornithologist and his paintings generated significant interest in birds and nature. The work of Archibald Thorburn, Allan Brooks, and Bruno Liljefors, by contrast, was often based on studies of live animals or sketches made in the field; their paintings married aesthetic quality and rigorous observation to give a vivid sense of the subject's character and its place in its environment.

The nineteenth century was the golden age of ornithology. Natural history was a great passion; everybody collected specimens and everyone wanted to know what to name them. It was difficult to compare one bird on a page to another on a different page, so artists began to put several similar species on the same page for comparison. This was the core of illustrations for monographs – long detailed, scholarly studies on one taxon (group of organisms), reviewing all the known species of that group, and synthesizing all that is known about them, such as Richard Bowdler Sharpe's *Monograph of the Alcedinidae: or, Family of Kingfishers*, illustrated by John Gerrard Keulemans.

In 1883 the American Ornithologists' Union was established, largely for the purpose of untangling bird nomenclature. Ornithologists such as taxonomist Robert Ridgway, after thorough studies, changed many long-used names, occasionally annoying a few other ornithologists in the process. Coming to conclusions by studying stuffed specimens, Ridgway and his ilk were called "closet ornithologists" by some field ornithologists.

As individual or patron-funded expeditions diminished, governments established funding for specific purposes; however, with government funding hard to come by, expeditions became more focused and particular goals expected. It was important to do more than just bring a bunch of specimens and pictures back; there had to be a systematic way of integrating this new knowledge into the existing framework of science. Artists were now not just reflecting scientific endeavours but becoming part of them – as did Louis Agassiz Fuertes and Robert Ridgway.

PREVIOUS PAGE: John Gerrard Keulemans, *Ceratogymna elata* (yellow-casqued hornbill), date unknown.

ABOVE: Sketch by Robert Ridgway, date unknown.

OPPOSITE: Allan Cyril Brooks, *A Water Turkey, Mexican Cormorant and a Mexican Grebe* – or anhinga (*Anhinga anhinga*), neotropic cormorant or olivaceous cormorant (*Phalacrocorax brasilianus*), Clark's grebe (*Aechmophorus clarkii*) in flight, and horned grebe (*Podiceps nigricollis*) swimming, 1934.

♀   2/3   ♂

JOHN GERRARD KEULEMANS
Dutch, 1842–1912

John Gerrard Keulemans was Dutch but for most of his life worked in England. From 1870 to 1900 hardly any ornithological work of importance was complete without illustrations by Keulemans.

Born in Rotterdam in 1842, Keulemans had his love of natural history and drawing encouraged by his parents. After developing his art skills, he was employed at the Leiden Museum at just 18 years of age. When he was 20, he was given the opportunity to travel to Africa on a collecting trip in 1864. Returning to Leiden, he published 200 lithographs for his first book, *Our Birds in House and Town*, between 1869 and 1876. He also wrote the text that described both wild and caged birds of the Netherlands.

By the nineteenth century, Britain had become a major supplier of fine bird books. Bird specimens were being imported from all over the British Empire, and artists were needed to illustrate them. Therefore, in 1869 Keulemans moved to London and was hired to illustrate Richard Bowdler Sharpe's *Monograph of the Alcedinidae; or, Family of Kingfishers,* a work that made Keulemans famous. He remained in England for the rest of his life but he continued to travel, including through most of Europe, bolstered by his ability to speak five languages.

Keulemans was probably the most prolific artist of the nineteenth century, as he contributed to at least 115 books and journals and produced four to five thousand illustrations. He regularly illustrated *Proceedings of the Zoological Society* of London and *Ibis*, the journal of the British Ornithological Union, to which he contributed every year from 1869 to 1909. He painted more extinct birds than any artist of his time. Keulemans illustrated many monographs, for which accurate illustrations are essential. In a monograph on the family of sunbirds, the author G E Shelley lauds Keulemans's illustrations, saying that his "name is sufficient guarantee for the accuracy of the details ..." Keulemans also illustrated taxonomic monographs on barbets, shorebirds, bee-eaters, cranes, petrels, rollers and lories. Monographs on the birds of particular locations were also enhanced by his art: *The Birds of Ceylon* (1880), *The Birds of Australia* (1910–27, posthumously), *The Avifauna of Laysan* (1893), and *A History of the Birds of New Zealand* (1873). He mostly produced lithographs, some in black and white. For colour, hand painting was usually carried out by semi-skilled artists in an assembly line. Although Keulemans's work was highly regarded, there was no guarantee that the colouring of others was up to his standard.

Keulemans described the Cape Verde warbler, a small brown bird of the Cape Verde group of islands off the west coast of Africa. He also contributed to a description of a rare ibis on the island of Principe. His notes on these birds indicated that he was an excellent field observer.

Keulemans was a believer in spiritualism at a time when the idea and its attendant séances were popular. Later in life he was disillusioned by the dishonesty he saw in spiritualism and used his scientific knowledge to expose the fraudulent activities of mediums, as did Harry Houdini a decade later.

ABOVE: John Gerrard Keulemans, *Todiramphus venerates* (Tahiti Kingfisher), from Richard Bowdler Sharpe's *A Monograph of the Alcedinidae, or Family of Kingfishers* (1868–71).

OPPOSITE: John Gerrard Keulemans, *Huia*, from W L Buller's *A History of the Birds of New Zealand* (1887–88). The Huia is extinct today.

OVERLEAF LEFT: John Gerrard Keulemans, *Blue-bellied Roller*, from Henry Eeles Dresser's *A Monograph of the Coraciidae, or Family of the Rollers* (1893).

OVERLEAF ABOVE: John Gerrard Keulemans, *Pycnonotus melanicterus, Black-capped Bulbul*, from William Vincent Legge's *A History of the Birds of Ceylon* (1878).

OVERLEAF BELOW: John Gerrard Keulemans, *Laysan Rail*, from Lionel Rothschild's *Avifauna of Laysan* (1893).

BLUEBELLIED ROLLER
CORACIAS CYANOGASTER

Hanhart imp

ART AND SCIENCE OVERLAP

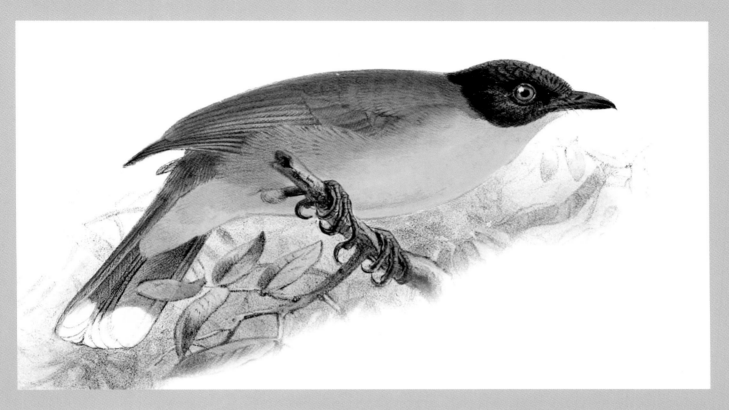

ROBERT RIDGWAY
American, 1850–1929

Robert Ridgway was an avian taxonomist – an ornithologist specializing in the classification of birds. In 1880 he became the first full-time curator of birds at the United States National Museum of the Smithsonian and later one of the founders of the American Ornithologists' Union. He described more North American bird species than did any other ornithologist of that time. Ridgway painted and drew birds to complement his writing.

Ridgway was born the eldest of 10 children, whose parents passed on their interest in the outdoors to all their offspring. His father was especially knowledgeable about birds, and his mother bought him several books about animals, and by Audubon (see page 86), and Wilson (see page 76). Ridgway began to sketch colour drawings before he turned four years of age.

At the age of 14, Ridgway mailed a letter to the patent office in Washington DC, enclosing a drawing of a bird that he could not identify. The letter got to Spencer Fullerton Baird, Assistant Secretary of The Smithsonian Institution, who identified the purple finch. Ridgway and Baird kept in touch, and three years later Baird had Ridgway appointed as a naturalist in Clarence King's geographical survey of the 40th Parallel, during which the team explored Nevada, Utah, and Idaho. Two years after that he was hired to write technical descriptions and illustrate *A History of North American Birds*, written by Baird and Thomas Brewer.

In 1874 Ridgway was appointed as an ornithologist at the Smithsonian. By 1882 the collection of bird skins at the Smithsonian numbered over 50,000, so he had plenty of potential research projects. He eventually published *A Catalogue of the Birds of North America* in 1880, which established his credibility in the field of ornithology.

Ridgway then published a *Manual of North American Birds* in 1887, condensing what was known about each species into 642 pages illustrated by 464 drawings. It was apparently meant to be a field guide, but its identification keys depended on having a bird in the hand, not field marks, so even though its illustrations were superb, it was not actually useful in the field.

Robert Ridgway's defining work on bird systematics was the 11-volume, 6,000-page *The Birds of North and Middle America*, published by the Smithsonian between 1901 and 1950. The main purpose of the work was to resolve problems of naming and classification. During his lifetime, no other ornithologist described as many new bird species as did Ridgway.

ART AND SCIENCE OVERLAP

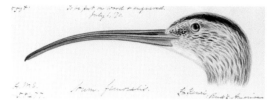

Having amassed considerable experience in bird portraiture and in writing detailed descriptions of birds, Ridgway realized that there needed to be some standardization of colours and colour names. Therefore, in 1886 he published the *Nomenclature of Colors for Naturalists, and Compendium for Useful Knowledge for Ornithologists.* Ten plates in the book displayed 186 colours that became a standard among ornithologists. He also included useful descriptions of feather patterns.

In 1912 he produced a larger book that contained 1,115 colours and that became a standard not just for naturalists but also for paint, chemical, and wallpaper manufacturers. With so many colours, Ridgway invented some novel names, including Dragon's-blood red and Bradley's blue. This new colour technology was not quite perfect, however; one colour, "Scheele's green", was a dangerous mix of arsenic and copper.

Ridgway published his first paper at the age of 18, and over the next 60 years he wrote about 550 books and articles, mainly on North American birds. His contributions as a taxonomist and writer have overshadowed his skills as an artist, but some of his best paintings can still be found in obscure books such as Nehrling's *Our Native Birds of Song and Beauty* and Nelson's *Contributions to the Natural History.*

Five birds carry scientific names that honour Ridgway, such as the Buff-collared nightjar, *Caprimulgus ridgwayi*, in addition to two birds with common names: Ridgway's rail and Ridgway's hawk.

TOP LEFT: Robert Ridgway, *Chestnut-sided Shrike Vireo*, date unknown. Native to Guatemala and Mexico.

TOP CENTRE: Robert Ridgway, *Whimbrel*, date unknown. Breeds in the far north.

TOP RIGHT: Robert Ridgway, *Dendrocygna fulva* (now *Dendrocygna bicolour*), fulvous whistling-duck, date unknown.

ABOVE LEFT: Robert Ridgway, *Dendroica dominica*, the yellow-throated warbler, date unknown.

ABOVE RIGHT: Robert Ridgway, *Loxigilla portericensis* (now *portoricensis*), Puerto Rican bullfinch, date unknown.

ARCHIBALD THORBURN
Scottish, 1860–1935

Archibald Thorburn was born in Edinburgh, a son of Robert Thorburn, who painted miniatures for Queen Victoria. Early on, Archibald was fascinated by nature and sketched leaves, flowers, and other natural history items, tutored by his father. Thorburn studied in Edinburgh before moving to London to enrol in St John's Wood Art School.

He took lessons from and was greatly inspired by prominent ornithological artist Joseph Wolf (see page 110). Thorburn also frequently returned to Scotland to study and paint wildlife in the field. At the age of 20, Thorburn had his first exhibition at the Royal Academy. Two years later he illustrated J E Harting's *Sketches of Bird Life* and then in 1883 *Familiar Wild Birds* by W Swaysland. Shortly after that he was commissioned to illustrate *Coloured Figures of Birds in the British Isles* by Lord Lilford, one of the founders of the British Ornithologists' Union. About half of the 421 illustrations were created by J G Keulemans (see page 122), and Thorburn produced the remaining 268. The book established his reputation for accuracy and detail; after its publication in 1888, demand for Thorburn's work increased dramatically.

Leonard Howard Lord Irby was a British ornithologist, Army officer, and apparently a good shot, collecting birds for study and food. While stationed at Gibraltar, Irby was encouraged by Lord Lilford to produce *Ornithology of the Straits of Gibraltar*; this book was published in 1895 and illustrated by Thorburn.

In 1925 Thorburn published the four-volume *British Birds,* which he both wrote and illustrated with watercolours. A review of the work states that the text is sparse but that the plates are "wholly delightful". He also painted in oil, but after 1900 worked mainly in watercolour because he felt that this medium more accurately depicted the softness of feathers.

Contemporary bird artist Rodger McPhail, considered to be Thornburn's successor, admires Thorburn's work for the life he put into his subjects. The habitat, the season, the weather, and the interaction of birds with each other imbue his work with realism. Some of his best paintings showed birds in flight, a subject that many painters avoided because of the difficulty in depicting wing attitude and feather positions correctly. The founder of the Thorburn Museum in Cornwall considers Thorburn the first British artist to combine scientific accuracy with "the fresh softness of the living bird". Archibald Thorburn paintings "portray the textures of feathers more brilliantly than anyone else," said Peter Scott, eminent British naturalist and son of Robert Falcon Scott of Antarctic fame.

After the end of the First World War, a new process of photographic reproduction came into being, partially replacing lithographs. Thorburn was one of the first wildlife artists to have his work reproduced by this method. The four-

OPPOSITE: Archibald Thorburn, *Eurasian Sparrowhawk*, from Thorburn's second edition of *British Birds, Vol. 2* (1925).

ABOVE: Archibald Thorburn, finches and allies, from Lord Lilford's *British Birds* (1918).

A. Thorburn

Litho. W. Greve, Berlin.

1/6

A. Thorburn
1920

volume study *A Monograph of the Pheasants*, published by William Beebe from 1918 to 1922, used both lithographs and photographs of oil paintings, illustrated by Thorburn, Fuertes, and others. A novel component of the work was a number of actual photographs of the pheasants' habitats.

Archibald Thorburn became a favourite of both King Edward VII and King George V. He participated in many hunting parties, including some at Sandringham, at the invitation of the king. In the latter part of his life, however, he became disillusioned by the distress calls of a hare he had shot, and his attitude changed; he became a conservationist. In 1927 he became Vice President of the Royal Society for the Protection of Birds. From 1930 until his death, Thorburn lived in Hascombe, Surrey, where he eschewed electrical connections to his home, preferring natural light in which to paint.

BRUNO LILJEFORS

Swedish, 1860–1939

One of the most influential wildlife artists of the late nineteenth and early twentieth centuries, Bruno Liljefors is perhaps best known for exciting paintings that show a predator stalking or killing prey.

From a poor family, the young Liljefors was noticed for his talent by local shopkeepers, who donated art materials to encourage him. He eventually enrolled at the Royal Swedish Academy of Fine Arts in Stockholm and three years later travelled through Europe, learning to draw animals, particularly birds and cats.

Liljefors's style changed over the years. At first his paintings were small, with an influence of Japanese art, in which the goal was reflecting spirituality rather than realism. Other paintings revealed an influence of impressionism, as in his *Swans on the Beach*, which focused on capturing a feeling rather than the details of the birds.

ART AND SCIENCE OVERLAP

Later paintings evolved into larger formats with broader and more unflinching
nature scenes. Instead of a pastoral, peaceful portrayal, the feeling was one of
survival, "nature, red in tooth and claw". A cat catching a chaffinch, a cat with a
young bird in its mouth, and a fox feeding a duck to its litter of cubs are certainly
different from the work of most bird painters who came before. His message
seems to be that animals live in a dangerous world.

Liljefors was a hunter, closely observing animals as he stalked them, often
killing them. His *Hawk and Black-Game* painting was based on specimens he had
shot. Like Audubon, he wired them into lifelike positions for painting. Positioning
the hawk and grouse in bushes, he actually painted a still life.

The "black-game" bird is actually the western capercaillie, also called the
wood grouse. Found across Eurasia, this largest of all grouse is a ground-living
forest bird especially prized by hunters. (In Germany, the quota for killing an
"*auerhahn*" is one in a lifetime.) Dark grey with metallic breast feathers and a
red eye ring, the male is quite spectacular. Males gather in the spring on a lek, or
courting ground, and display and call to attract a female half their size. The look
and behaviour of the Capercaillie attracted more artists than most other bird

species in Europe and the birds are depicted on stamps, coats of arms, flags, and all manner of other artworks. Liljefors's most successful painting of this genre is the large-scale *Capercaillie Lek*, 1888, in which he captures the ambience of the forest at dawn.

Liljefors maintained a considerable menagerie, including foxes, eagles, hares, squirrels, and owls. Painting from life, death, and captivity provided him with a variety of mental images to create his works. Putting birds in natural scenes was common by the twentieth century, but his paintings took realism one step further, such as depicting camouflage. In his painting *Forest Scene with Pine Marten Attacking a Black Grouse Hen*, it takes the viewer a few moments to figure out what is happening, but then the scene leaps right off the canvas. It gives one the impression of being there and surprised by the appearance of wildlife.

Liljefors's *Common Swifts*, showing two swifts flying over a field of wildflowers, would challenge today's high-speed photographer. They are the product of hours of fieldwork, skin study, and close observation. His painting *Cat and Chaffinch*, based on live and dead specimens, is similarly lifelike, although this would be a rare sight in life.

At the age of 65 Liljefors was awarded Sweden's most prestigious recognition, the Tessin Medal. Today, a hundred years after their creation, his works are still considered some of the finest in the history of wildlife art.

TOP: Bruno Liljefors, *Eagle Owl Hunting a Hare*, 1931. Both the hare and the owl have colours that help them blend into the background, so it takes a few seconds to see what is happening in the painting.

ABOVE: Bruno Liljefors, *Black Grouse (Capercaillie) Mating Game in the Moss*, 1907.

OPPOSITE: Bruno Liljefors, *Cat and Chaffinch*, 1885. A painting from a composite of living and dead animals that would almost be impossible for a photograph to capture.

Allan Brooks.

ALLAN CYRIL BROOKS
English/Canadian, 1869–1946

Born in India, Allan Brooks spent his early years influenced by his father, a keen birdwatcher who collected Indian bird specimens for the British Museum.

When Brooks was about five, he was sent to England to live with his grandparents. There, he received some tutoring from his father's friend, John Hancock, a naturalist, ornithologist, and "the father of modern taxidermy", who introduced excitement into taxidermy subjects, such as a predator mouthing its prey. Hancock was also an artist and writer, and edited Thomas Bewick's *A History of British Birds*. Thus, Allan Brooks had an early introduction to both nature and art.

Brooks's family moved to a farm in Canada in 1881. Allan's father, William, received visits from various professional ornithologists; Allan learned taxidermy, bird and egg collecting, and field observation from the visitors and began painting birds around the farm. William Brewster, ornithologist and co-founder of the American Ornithologists' Union, asked Brooks to prepare some watercolours for him. Brooks had never had art lessons, but he studied the work of some of the renowned bird illustrators, such as Joseph Wolf (see page 110) and J G Keulemans (see page 122).

Brooks travelled around north-western Canada, trapping, observing, and sketching birds. He corresponded with naturalists in Canada and the United States, earning a little money by supplying specimens to collectors and museums. Robert Ridgway (see page 126), curator of birds at the Smithsonian Institution, was one such contact, helping Brooks identify birds that Brooks sent him. Specimen collection was not very lucrative, however, so in 1897 Brooks began to sell sketches and articles about birds to minor journals.

In 1906 Brooks was contacted by ornithologist William Dawson, who asked him to illustrate *The Birds of Washington*. Published in 1909, this book contained photographs, sketches, and black-and white illustrations of birds, nests, eggs, and habitat, with written descriptions.

Being a good shot with a rifle, Brooks left at the age of 45 for England and the First World War. He was promoted to major and received the Distinguished Service Order, but he never stopped sketching birds. After the war he returned to Canada and found further work as an artist: he made a series of illustrations for Florence Bailey's *Birds of New Mexico* and illustrated Dawson's *The Birds of California* in 1923, Percy Tavener's *Birds of Western Canada* in 1926, and *Birds of Canada* in 1934. That year Brooks and his wife Marjorie began a world tour of birdwatching and sketching.

ABOVE: Allan Cyril Brooks, *Indian Spot-bill, Australian Duck, Eastern Spot-billed Duck, and Philippine Mallard*, from John C Phillips's *A Natural History of the Ducks* (1922–26).

OPPOSITE: Allan Cyril Brooks, *Various Ibis Perch Lakeside*, 1932. Showing White, Scarlet, and White-faced Ibises.

Allan Brooks

ABOVE: Allan Cyril Brooks, *Two Swallow-tailed Kites*, 1933.

OPPOSITE: Allan Cyril Brooks, *Strawberry Finches, a Bengali Finch and Java Sparrows*, date unknown. All Asian species.

In 1920 Allan Brooks met Louis Agassiz Fuertes (see page 140) at a meeting of the American Ornithologists' Union. They became friends – Brooks spent a month at Fuertes's studio – and worked together on John C Phillips's *A Natural History of the Ducks*. They deliberately made their styles similar, but there were major differences. Fuertes did illustrations for scientific works and the details were very lifelike, but the paintings had little or no background. Brooks included a background and foreground, especially mountains and skies, and depicted the essence of a bird rather than detail. Unlike Fuertes, Brooks struggled financially, partly because he had to cater to publishers' needs, which did not always align with the requirements of bird illustration. In some cases he had to put too many birds on one page, thus interfering with the composition.

Brooks was offered jobs by major museums, but he preferred to be a freelance artist. His bird skins and egg collections comprised a minor museum in themselves, serving as his library and reference collection. The labels on all specimens had all the important information. He was so insistent on these details that he published a paper on their importance.

LOUIS AGASSIZ FUERTES
Puerto Rican–American, 1874–1927

The most prolific American bird artist since Audubon (see page 86), ornithologist Louis Agassiz Fuertes was named after Louis Agassiz, the Swiss-American biologist and geologist who was born several decades earlier. Fuertes's father was an astronomer and engineer at Cornell University, New York, an institution with a distinguished ornithology programme. Fuertes grew up in Ithaca, the home of Cornell, and graduated from the university.

As a child Fuertes admired Audubon and developed an interest in birds, which, unfortunately, included killing them with a slingshot. He studied their forms, feathers, and habits, and began to draw them. At the age of 14 he painted his first bird, a red crossbill. At the age of 17 he became the youngest associate member of the American Ornithologists' Union. Today Fuertes's drawing of the great auk appears on the cover of the AOU's journal, *The Auk*.

In 1892 he travelled with his parents to Europe, sketching birds and other animals in Paris. He attended school in Zurich for a year and then returned to Cornell to study architecture. While he was still at university he met eminent ornithologist Elliott Coues, who would support and promote his work. Later he became an apprentice with Abbott Thayer, an artist and naturalist best known for his paintings of angels. Both he and Thayer were fascinated by birds and exchanged study skins. Thayer introduced Fuertes to the idea of countershading, in which animals make themselves less obvious by being light or white below and dark above. Fuertes took that to heart and demonstrated that feature in some of his paintings, such as the Swainson's Warbler. He wrote to George Sutton, a young artist whom he mentored for a few weeks, about depicting countershading in paintings.

C Hart Merriam, director of the US Biological Survey, chose Fuertes to accompany the 1899 Harriman Alaska Expedition. Harriman, a wealthy railroad magnate, supported a group of artists, scientists, photographers, and naturalists to explore the coast of Alaska from Seattle to Siberia. Included were John Muir, the Sierra Club founder; George Bird Grinnell, anthropologist, naturalist, and one of the founders of the Audubon Society; and Robert Ridgway (see page 126), curator of birds at the National Museum. This gave the young Fuertes the opportunity to see a new part of the world and associate with influential and experienced people. His enthusiasm and congeniality endeared him to the members of the expedition. In two months he travelled over 4,000 miles (6,440 km), collected over 100 specimens, and returned with a large portfolio of pencil sketches and watercolours.

ABOVE: Louis Agassiz Fuertes, *Red Crossbill*, 1903. A later painting of the first species he painted, at the age of 14.

OPPOSITE: Louis Agassiz Fuertes, *Passenger Pigeons and Mourning Doves*, c.1920–27.

Louis Agassiz Fuertes

L. G. Fuertes

His next trip was to south-western Texas in 1901. During this four-month trip, Fuertes developed a style that characterized many of his paintings: birds were the central focus of the painting, and the background was complementary. A good example is his shrike painting where two pairs of shrikes are perched on a thin thorn branch forming an X at the focus of the painting.

Audubon died about 50 years before Fuertes began his career, and for most of those years there was an absence of high-quality bird painting in the United States. Fuertes's field experience and use of freshly caught specimens provided lifelike values to his work, and after the 1890s his art was much in demand. Fuertes was able to recreate realistic and intimate poses reflecting life. He also conveyed scientific information in his paintings, such as the curlew sandpiper standing on one leg to conserve body heat.

ABOVE: Louis Agassiz Fuertes, *A Pair of Gadwalls*, or *Anas strepera*, 1915.

OPPOSITE LEFT: Louis Agassiz Fuertes, *A Pair of Black Flycatchers*, also known as *Phainopepla*, 1914.

OPPOSITE RIGHT: Unknown artist, *Fuertes Parrot* (*Ilapalopsittaca fuertesi*), c.1900, named after Louis Agassiz Fuertes.

ART AND SCIENCE OVERLAP

Fuertes travelled over much of the United States and to dozens of countries. He illustrated parts or all of 35 of bird books and 60 other publications, such as the *National Geographic*, for both scientific and lay audiences. He helped the conservation movement through a series of collectors' cards distributed in Arm and Hammer Baking Soda boxes in the 1920s and 30s.

Fuertes's early paintings formed a cornerstone of a classic work of nature-writing for young people: *Citizen Bird*. This book, published in 1897 – the joint creation of ornithologist Elliott Coues; a nature-writer, Mabel Osgood Wright; and Fuertes, who provided 111 illustrations – links science, aesthetics, and ethics to encourage popular ornithology and promoted much of the grass-roots support for conservation measures at the turn of the twentieth century.

Fuertes's parrot, thought to be extinct until it was rediscovered in 2002, was named in commemoration of the artist.

C.G.Finch-Davies.
1 - 10 - 19.

Chapter Eight

BROADER APPEAL

———————

Until the late eighteenth century, interest in birds revolved mainly around their use as food or as decorative elements in paintings. But at the dawn of the Victorian era, birds became subjects of serious study. Exploration was reaching new heights, and the specimens brought back to Europe from the southern continents piqued the public's interest. Collecting bird skins and eggs, keeping caged birds, and acquiring bird art were common. Some naturalists and artists carried out studies and created art in the field, as did Charles Gibney Finch-Davies in southern Africa. Bird artists were also beginning to combine their painting skills with scientific knowledge to produce works of high technical and observational accuracy.

In 1904 a Bird-Land camera for wildlife photography appeared on the market, and in 1912 the first exposition of bird photography was held in London. Now birdwatchers, artists, and naturalists could bring home photos of birds in the wild. Bird ringing also became popular in the early twentieth century, so capturing birds alive for study replaced shooting them. Attitudes towards birds were changing, and watching birds began to replace their collection. In the late 1800s the first laws were passed to protect birds and habitats. In the United States, the federal Migratory Bird Treaty Act of 1918 was enacted in 1916 to implement a Convention between the United States and Great Britain (the latter acting for Canada) for the protection of migratory birds. More recently, in Europe, the Birds Directive of the EU, first passed in 1979, aims to protect European birds and habitats.

Ornithologists were starting to share their knowledge with a wider readership. The first field guide to birds in the United States was *Birds Through an Opera Glass* (1889) by Florence Bailey, and in 1905 Chester A Reed published a bird identification book that sold 600,000 copies. But there were dozens of other guides for local birds such as *Familiar Wild Birds* (of Scotland), published in 1883, with illustrations by Archibald Thorburn (see page 128). Ludlow Griscom published *Birds of the New York City Region* in 1923, and in 1931 Neville William Cayley (see page 156) wrote *What Bird is That?*, an enormously popular guide to the birds of Australia. In 1934, Roger Tory Peterson (see page 168) published *A Field Guide to the (Eastern) Birds*, which, along with its subsequent editions and spin-offs, has arguably become the model for all natural history field guides worldwide.

Field guides are both a result of and impetus for the public's enthusiasm for birds and bird art. Copies of Audubon's *Birds of America*, produced nearly two centuries ago, are still sought after today. Cayley's Australian bird book still attracts ardent interest; it went digital nearly 100 years after its first printing. Birdwatchers are keen collectors of any art related to birds – paintings, posters, sculptures, and all manner of accessories depicting these fascinating creatures. And, as can be seen in Peterson's career, illustrations and other forms of bird art have also generated a keen concern in the general public for environmental issues as a whole.

PREVIOUS PAGE: Claude
Gibney Finch-Davies,
Pelecanus onocrotalus, *Great
White Pelican*, 1918. From
his African birds sketchbook.

ABOVE: Roger Tory Peterson,
*James Flamingos in the
Andes*, date unknown.

LEFT: Lilian Marguerite
Medland, *Hooded Crow*,
c. 1906–11.

CLAUDE GIBNEY FINCH-DAVIES

British/South African, 1875–1920

Claude Gibney Davies was born in India, but was sent to England at the age of six to get a "proper education". Even then he had an interest in birds and sent drawings to his older sister in India.

At the age of 18, he went to South Africa, enlisted in the army, and remained. His duties took him to many parts of the continent; being in the military simply gave him a way to shoot and paint his way through Africa. He took careful notes on each bird he shot, including what they tasted like when he ate them.

Davies eventually married Aileen Finch. The name seemed appropriate to his interests, so he called himself "Finch-Davies" (the alternate explanation is that his in-laws applied pressure on him to do so).

More travel, more drawing, and more reading polished his skills, and by 1905 he had produced over 200 high-quality paintings in 10 volumes and developed an international reputation. He contributed to scientific journals and was one of the founders of the South African Ornithologists' Union. He painted many species of waterfowl and game birds and eventually half of the bird species of South Africa. At the peak of his career he was the best bird artist in southern Africa. His bird paintings were featured on a series of South African stamps.

The more Finch-Davies travelled, the more raptors entranced him. By 1911 he devoted much of his artwork to them; he eventually illustrated all the birds of prey that were known in Southern Africa at the time. Only eight more species have been found since. In his book co-authored with A C Kemp, *The Birds of Prey of Southern Africa*, he clarified the identification of the Red-headed Falcon. He also published other papers on raptors to clarify their relationships. He published *Gamebirds and Waterfowl of South Africa* with Major Boyd Horsbrugh in 1912. After the beginning of the First World War, Finch-Davies was sent to German South West Africa (Namibia), where his fellow soldiers brought him birds they had shot.

After a long correspondence with Austin Roberts, curator of birds and mammals at the Transvaal Museum in Pretoria, Finch-Davies started to spend time at the museum's library. Unfortunately, the museum ultimately discovered that he had torn 230 plates from the reference books he consulted. The director of the South African Museum in Cape Town also found 130 plates missing from reference books at that institution. Finch-Davies's paintings were kept at the Museum until he had paid for the replacement of the damaged books. His reputation was ruined and, severely depressed, he died at the age of 45.

Twenty years after his death, Austin Roberts decided to publish Finch-Davies's *Birds of South Africa*, which required 1,032 illustrations on 56 plates. Artist Norman Lighton was given Finch-Davies's plates to help him create the drawings. Unfortunately, it appears that many of Lighton's paintings were very good copies of Finch-Davies's paintings, except for minor changes. Despite his controversial actions in damaging the reference books, researchers are still citing Finch-Davies's work nearly a century after his death.

ABOVE: Claude Gibney Finch-Davies, *Bycanistes brevis*, silvery-cheeked hornbill, 1940.

OPPOSITE: Claude Gibney Finch-Davies, *Phoeniconaias minor* (now *Phoenicopterus*), lesser flamingo, 1919. From his African birds sketchbook.

C.G. Finch Davies.
21-12-1919.

ABOVE LEFT: Claude Gibney Finch-Davies, *Ayres's Hawk Eagle* (*Hieraaetus Ayresi*), 1919.

ABOVE: Claude Gibney Finch-Davies, *Swainson's Francolin* (Pternistes Swainson), from Major Boyd Horsbrugh's *The Game-birds and Water-fowl of South Africa* (1912).

LEFT: Claude Gibney Finch-Davies, *African Olive Pigeon* (*Columba arquatrix*), from Horsbrugh's *The Game-birds and Water-fowl of South Africa*.

OPPOSITE: Claude Gibney Finch-Davies, *African Open-bill* (*Anastomus lamelligerus*), 1918.

C.G.Finch-Davies.
30 - 6 - 18.

LILIAN MARGUERITE MEDLAND
English/Australian, 1880–1955

Lilian Medland was a nurse and illustrator of bird books. Born in London and educated by a governess, she loved drawing outdoors and cared for animals, raising a woodpecker in her studio. She left home at 16 to train as a nurse at Guy's Hospital in London. She also began painting miniatures.

O ne of the senior surgeons where she worked, Charles Stonham, was an ornithologist; in 1906, she began work with Stonham on illustrating 318 plates for his *Birds of the British Islands*. Not having previously worked as a professional artist, she spent a lot of time at London Zoo.

In 1911 she was invited to illustrate a revised edition of William Yarrell's *A History of British Birds*; although the work was never completed, the 248 paintings she had done were discovered in immaculate condition in 1972.

In 1923 Medland moved to Australia. She painted 30 species of birds for the Australian Museum, which were issued as postcards in 1925 and became very popular. The *Brisbane Courier Mail* noted that, "Each postcard is a triumph of colour illustration and should appeal to a very wide public, and one not confined to Australia by any means." Her scarlet honeyeater appeared on the front cover of the *Australian Museum Magazine* in October–December 1933.

In the 1930s she completed 53 plates depicting 883 Australian birds for Gregory Mathews's 12-volume *Birds of Australia*. Mathews's work, following that of John and Elizabeth Gould (see page 96), was taxonomic. Mathews included long descriptions and discussions of genera, species, and subspecies, more accurately and in more detail than the Goulds, although some of his names and descriptions were controversial. According to a review in 1927 in *The Auk,* Medland's illustrations were not nearly as good as those in the Goulds' work. But according to the Royal Zoological Society of New South Wales, "each bird was … painted scientifically accurately to a degree never equalled by other ornithological artists". The Society noted that Medland's illustrations in the book were so well done that even an amateur could identify the birds from them. She also created the plates for her husband Tom Iredale's books *Birds of Paradise and Bower Birds* (1950) and *Birds of New Guinea* (1956).

Mathews's and Medland's work was never finished, perhaps because of the competition from Neville William Cayley's Australian bird guide *What Bird is That?*. Medland, however, organized Mathews's guide by putting related birds together, as guides do today, while Cayley organized them by habitat. Both artists' works suffer a little from a lack of depth and appear flat. Medland was never accepted as part of the social scene, partly because she had lost her hearing after she contracted diphtheria in 1907. She died of cancer at her home at Queenscliffe in 1955. A biography of her life, *Seen But Not Heard*, was published in 2014 and includes all 53 plates from Gregory Mathews's unpublished handbook of Australian birds.

TOP: Lilian Marguerite Medland, *Great Grey Heron*, date unknown.

ABOVE: Lilian Marguerite Medland, *Crested Lark*, date unknown.

OPPOSITE: Lilian Marguerite Medland, illustration of tui, thrush and others for an unpublished work on New Zealand birds, c.1934.

OPPOSITE: Lilian Marguerite Medland, parrot illustrations for an unpublished book on Australian birds by Gregory M Mathews, c.1930–39.

LEFT: Lilian Marguerite Medland, *Lord Howe Island Petrels*, c.1930.

ABOVE: Lilian Marguerite Medland, *Sanderling*, 1909.

NEVILLE WILLIAM CAYLEY
Australian, 1886–1950

Neville H P Cayley (1853–1903) was well known for his paintings of game birds as well as magpies, blue wrens, and purportedly 1,500 pictures of kookaburras. He wanted to produce a book of all Australian birds that would be accessible to the average Australian, unlike the expensive volumes published by John and Elizabeth Gould 50 years before. His Australian Birds *was published in 1894–95, but was not successful.*

ABOVE: *Laughing Kookaburra* by Neville H P Cayley, father of Neville W Cayley, 1892.

OPPOSITE: Neville W Cayley, *Magnificent Riflebirds*, from his *What Bird is That?* (1931).

His more famous son was Neville William Cayley. At first, as he learned from his father, Cayley was satisfied simply to paint attractive pictures of birds, but as his skills developed his work became more technical.

Born in New South Wales, Neville W Cayley moved with his parents to Sydney in the 1890s. In 1918, he published his first work, a small booklet of seven birds and one page of text, entitled *Our Birds*. Later came *Our Flowers* in 1920 and *The Tale of Bluey Wren* in 1926. Then he began to illustrate birds' eggs for the *Australian Encyclopedia*. As his ornithological expertise built, his work became more serious and technical.

In 1931 Cayley, intending to complete his father's plans, published *What Bird is That?*, illustrating every Australian bird in watercolour – nearly 800 species on 36 plates. This was the first complete field guide of Australian birds. In octavo size, 9.5 by 6 inches, it was so successful that it was reprinted until the 1960s. Revised editions by ornithologist Terence Lindsey were regularly published, the latest in 2016. This update included about a hundred new species, totalling 430 plates, with range maps for each species and a description of each habitat. The only major difference between this book and today's guides is that it was organized by habitat rather than in evolutionary relationships as guides are now. An eBook with 832 colour pages, 769 birds, and 101 bird calls was made available in 2018.

Cayley's other major publications were *Finches in Bush and Aviary*, *Budgerigars in Bush and Aviary*, *Australian Parrots in Field and Aviary*, and *The Fairy Wrens of Australia*. He is applauded for his "careful and comprehensive summary of scientific data" on the species he described. His last work was his major opus, the "big bird book", which would have illustrated all the species, subspecies, plumages, and eggs of all known species in Australia. Unfortunately Cayley died before the book was finished, although most of the artwork was completed. Terence Lindsey took on the project, blending it with the *What Bird is That?* book.

Cayley served as president of both the Royal Zoological Society of New South Wales and the Royal Australasian Ornithologists' Union. He also published scientific papers in the Australian journal *Emu* and in *Emu – Austral Ornithology*, on both wild birds and the aviculture of some captive bird species.

OPPOSITE: Neville W Cayley, Scrubwrens, from *What Bird is That?* Top left: Large-billed Scrubwrens; bottom left: Yellow-throated Scrubwrens; right: White-browed Scrubwrens.

ABOVE: Neville W Cayley, *Australian Pelicans*, from *What Bird is That?*

RIGHT: Neville W Cayley, *Black-necked Stork or Jabiru*, from *What Bird is That?*

JESSIE ARMS BOTKE
American, 1883–1971

Jessie Arms Botke was born in Chicago, Illinois, and attended the Chicago Art Institute in 1897–98 and 1902–05. Following a trip to Europe in 1909, she returned to Chicago and listed her profession as "artist, interior decorating".

ABOVE: Jessie Arms Botke, *Egrets*, 1930.

OPPOSITE: Jessie Arms Botke, *White Peacock and Sulphur-crested Cockatoos*, date unknown.

She moved to New York in 1911 where she became a specialist in tapestry cartoons ("cartoon" here refers to the Italian *cartone*, which is a large sheet of paper used in preparation for a painting or tapestry). A student of Albert Herter, Botke worked at Herter Looms until 1915. At one time, Herter gave his artists the job of creating a peacock mural for the dining room in the home of actress Billie Burke (known for depicting the good witch Glinda in *The Wizard of Oz*, 1939) at Hastings-on-Hudson, New York. For this assignment, Botke studied peacocks at the Bronx Zoo; those visits kindled her interest in painting birds.

After moving to San Francisco, where she worked with Herter on a mural for the St Francis Hotel, she married Dutch artist Cornelius Botke and the couple moved to Carmel-by-the-Sea, California in 1919. They became influential figures in the local art colony there until they moved to Southern California in 1927, remaining in the area for the rest of their lives.

Botke's exotic, highly ornamental bird art features cranes, swans, geese, flamingoes, toucans, and many cockatoos and albino peacocks. The birds are shown in more or less natural settings, often with exquisitely detailed flowers or other greenery in the surrounding background or foreground, frequently embellished with gold or silver leaf. She worked in colour woodcut, gouache, watercolour, and oil, and designed and painted murals for schools, restaurants, hotels, and the I Magnin department store in Los Angeles.

White Peacocks and Magnolia on canvas with gold leaf is somewhat reminiscent of the early Dutch artists who used large white birds – swans, geese, or peacocks – as centrepieces for their works. *White Peacock and Sulphur-crested Cockatoos* brings to mind the work of Jakob Bogdani. Her many depictions of egrets, cranes, and peacocks loom large in the frame of the picture, the rest of the picture plane being occupied by luxurious vegetation. The birds are realistic, the vegetation slightly less so and as in *Manchurian Cranes*, an oil and gold leaf on masonite work, the water in which the birds stand is in the Impressionist style. Botke and Janet Turner (see page 176), who came along a few decades later, both fill the frames of their paintings, leaving little open space to spare, to the extent of the image being abstracted. There is no firm indication Turner was influenced by Botke, although both spent the bulk of their careers in California.

ABOVE LEFT: Jessie Arms Botke, *Sacred Cranes in a Tropical River*, date unkown.

ABOVE RIGHT: Jessie Arms Botke, *White Peacocks and Magnolia*, date unkown.

OPPOSITE: Jessie Arms Botke, *Manchurian Cranes*, date unknown.

Botke was a member of the Chicago Society of Artists, Women Painters and Sculptors, the California Art Club, the California Watercolour Society, the American Watercolour Society, and the Foundation of Western Art. She won numerous awards for her work, including high distinction from the Art Institute of Chicago.

In her recent book, *Emerging from the Shadows*, Maurine St Gaudens features 320 women artists working in California from 1860 to 1960. The artists were chosen both for their artistic merit as well as their role in furthering art culture in California. For many of the artists profiled in the book, any recognition or acknowledgement they received during their lifetime was fleeting, and this was certainly the case for Jessie Arms Botke.

ENNION.

ERIC ENNION
British, 1900–81

Eric Ennion, the son of an English country doctor, grew up near Cambridge, where he explored the countryside and its wildlife from an early age. As a young boy fascinated by birds, he drew them by copying from books. He also made a little money by catching house sparrows and turning them in for a bounty from local farmers.

Learning how to hunt and shoot developed his skills in stalking and observing. When Eric expressed an interest in painting birds as a career, his father took him to visit Archibald Thorburn (see page 128). Thorburn advised Eric that he should follow in his father's footsteps instead, so Eric pursued a medical degree at Cambridge and joined his father's medical practice. Shortly afterwards his father passed away, so he took over the practice.

But Ennion never lost the desire to paint. He would watch birds and make sketches while on his rounds. Unlike most artists who make quick sketches in the field and fill in the details later, Ennion made detailed sketches in the field with pen, pencil, and even watercolours of live birds. He could sketch quickly, on an envelope or napkin if nothing else was handy. He built up a large collection of sketches and illustrations from magazines. He also prepared skins and dissected dead birds to become familiar with their anatomy.

In 1941 Ennion wrote and illustrated *The Animal World – Its Attack and Defence*, followed by *Adventurer's Fen* in 1942. In 1943 he published *The British Bird*, simply illustrated with 15 full-page plates and 50 line drawings. He ultimately wrote and illustrated 11 books. At the end of the Second World War, Ennion sold his medical practice and served as warden of a field studies centre at Flatford in Suffolk; five years later, in 1950, he and his wife established a Field Centre and Bird Observatory in Northumberland, where he observed and ringed birds as well as teaching art. He later explored the Netherlands, Iceland, Sweden, and the Canary Islands. In 1961 he and his wife moved south again, to Wiltshire.

Ennion co-founded the Society of Wildlife Artists and organized an exhibition of British bird painting at the 14th International Ornithological Congress at Oxford in 1966. He continued to teach, exhibit, and write through the 1970s, up to his death in 1981.

OPPOSITE: Eric Ennion, *Birds*, from Richard Morse's *Life in Pond and Stream* (1943).

RIGHT: Eric Ennion, *Bearded Tits*, 1950.

ABOVE: Eric Ennion, *Winter Flock on Flooded Fields*, from his book *The Lapwing* (1949). Eric Ennion: "So there is method in this seeming February madness of a Lapwing flock ... All are now expressing their desires, and thus indicating their degree of inner ripeness ... Small wonder there appears to be confusion!"

OPPOSITE: Eric Ennion, *Ducks*, from Morse's *Life in Pond and Stream*.

Eric Ennion is generally considered one of the most influential bird artists of the twentieth century. His birds were not particularly realistic, often a rough likeness, but their personalities showed through. Former editor of *Birds* magazine Rob Hume said that Ennion painted "jizz" to perfection. "Jizz", a word invented by birdwatchers, is the overall impression or appearance of a bird gathered from its shape, posture, size, colouration, movement, voice, habitat, and location. ("Jizz" began as "giss", "general impression of size and shape", but somehow was transformed to "jizz".) Ennion wanted people to look at his illustrations and understand the energy in the bird's life.

Fellow wildlife artist John Busby visited Ennion frequently and became a master artist himself with Ennion's help and encouragement. Writing in a biography of Ennion, *The Living Birds of Eric Ennion*, he observed, "I doubt if any animal or bird painter has ever logged so many hours of watching." He wrote that Ennion is regarded by many artists as the "supreme example to follow".

ROGER TORY PETERSON

American, 1908–96

A birding legend, Roger Tory Peterson was an ornithologist, artist, author, and photographer. Born in Jamestown, New York, he joined an Audubon club when he was 12 years old. He woke at dawn and watched birds while making newspaper deliveries. In seventh grade his teacher gave his class a bird outline to colour; Peterson claimed later that colouring that blue jay convinced him to be a bird painter.

After graduating from high school in 1925 he attended his first American Ornithologists' Union meeting and met his idol, Louis Agassiz Fuertes. Peterson took art classes in New York and then taught art and natural history at summer camps, eventually taking a full-time job as a teacher at a prestigious boys' school.

LEFT: Roger Tory Peterson, *Penguins*, date unknown.

OPPOSITE LEFT: Roger Tory Peterson, *Two Mandarin Ducks*, date unknown.

OPPOSITE RIGHT: Roger Tory Peterson, *Hooded Warbler*, date unknown.

Frustrated by existing bird guides, Peterson decided to write his own. He drew the birds so that the most important features for identification, now called "field marks", were shown and described in the text. After he was turned down by several publishers, Houghton-Mifflin took a chance and in 1934 printed 2,000 copies of *A Field Guide to the (Eastern) Birds*. They sold out immediately. In 1941 a western edition was added. Today the Peterson Field Guide series comprises dozens of field guides, by various authors, for seashells, lizards, fish, and rocks, as well as birds.

Peterson's guide was not the first. In 1889 Florence Merriam published *Birds Through an Opera Glass*, and in 1902 she published the *Handbook of Birds of the Western United States* under her married name Florence Merriam Bailey. However, at nearly 500 pages long, with 33 full-page plates by Louis Agassiz Fuertes (see page 140), illustrations by Robert Ridgway (see page 126), and 600 uncoloured woodcuts, this book was too big to carry into the field. In addition, its illustrations, including photos of study skins, left much to be desired. By contrast, in 1904 Ralph Hoffmann published *A Guide to the Birds of New England and Eastern New York*, which described field marks, habitat, and behaviour in the same way as modern-day field guides.

In addition to his books, Peterson painted and wrote several articles for *Life* magazine; his writing made bird science easily accessible to the public. Drafted into the Army Air Corps in 1943, he also used his field guide experience to

produce a plane-spotting manual. In 1948 he wrote *Birds over America* and in 1950 received the John Burroughs Medal, the first of many literary awards for nature writing. In 1954 he illustrated and co-authored *A Field Guide to the Birds of Britain and Europe*. Peterson wrote other, more general books such as *Wildlife in Colour*, *Wild America*, and *The Birds* and co-authored *The World of Birds* with James Fisher.

This work as an artist and naturalist led Peterson to become an environmental advocate, urging protection of birds against problems such as DDT, pollution, and habitat destruction. A founder of the World Wildlife Fund, he received numerous accolades for his conservationist work, including the American Ornithologists' Union Brewster Medal, the Gold Medal of the New York Zoological Society, and the Presidential Medal of Freedom. He was also a photographer, but continued to draw throughout his life.

Peterson's art allowed him to reach a wide audience to spread the word about the importance of saving birds. His contribution to environmental knowledge was noted by American biologist Paul Ehrlich, who wrote that, "In this century, no one has done more to promote an interest in living creatures than Roger Tory Peterson, the inventor of the modern field guide".

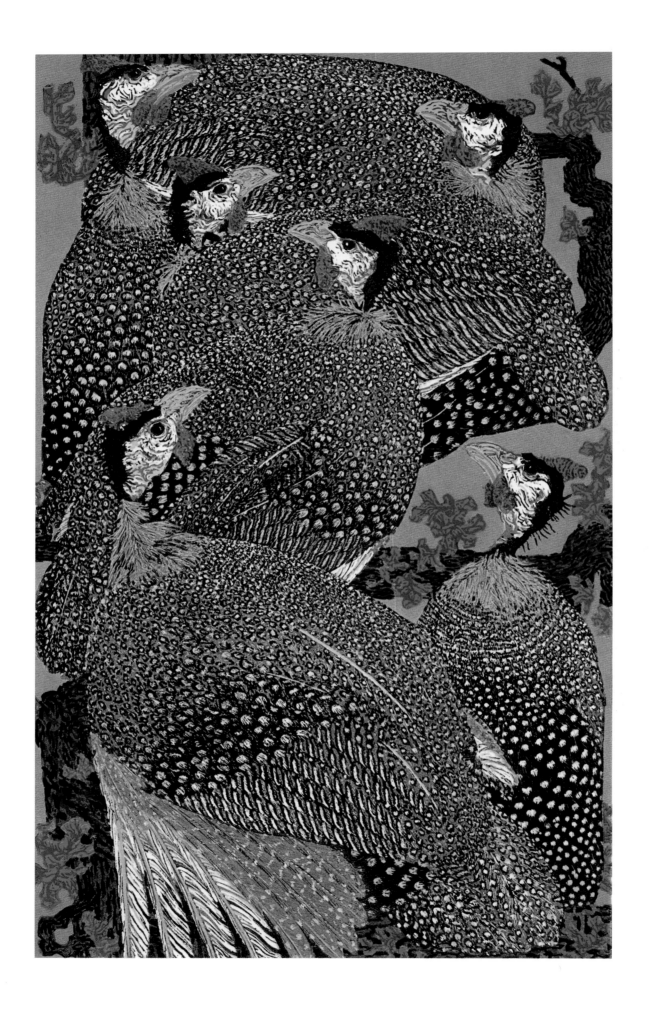

Chapter Nine

BIRD ART SUPPORTS BIRDS

———

PREVIOUS PAGE: Janet Turner, *Guinea Fowl*, 1950. A perfect example of Turner's full frame composition.

ABOVE: Keith Shackleton, *Wild Swans in the Surf*, 1949.

OPPOSITE: Arthur B Singer, illustrations of various seabirds, date unknown.

Silent Spring, written by US conservationist Rachel Carson and published in 1962, helped to publicize the dangers of pesticides and galvanize the environmental movement. The decline of brown pelicans, peregrine falcons, and bald eagles in the United States and peregrine falcons and sparrowhawks in the United Kingdom were the most obvious signs of the effect of toxic chemicals on the environment. Birds became the symbol of the environmental movement and to a great extent still are. Bird artists have been helping the environment simply by making available attractive or interesting bird images that encourage the public to appreciate nature.

Arthur Singer illustrated a number of books for the lay reader, such as *Life of the Hummingbird*, but his art made an especially significant impact as illustrations in the *Golden Field Guide to Birds of North America*. This was a very popular guide that often converted casual observers of nature into birdwatchers.

Canadian James Lansdowne and Australian William Cooper illustrated books for amateur naturalists in their respective hemispheres. Keith Shackleton's art, based on his trips to the polar regions, delivered messages about the cold, stark world above and below us.

Janet Turner's prints are recognizable and not unrealistic, but neither are they lifelike. They are the tools she used to create a scene that seems to have a different message for every viewer. Instead of making a bird or group of birds the subject of a picture, they often *are* the picture, filling the frame. She asks people to view and respect birds in a different way, and they do. A respected teacher of art, Turner was also an avid conservationist.

The days of scientific illustration continue, but they have changed. In the Renaissance, whole birds were drawn mainly for the purpose of comparison and classification, although there was no system to organize them. Today we have sorted out avian classification schemes, albeit with a continual tweaking of taxons as we learn new things. Illustrated bird books today are published not for scientific content but for enjoyment, whether a field guide or just a book of pictures. One never tires of seeing a bald eagle soaring over the forest or a colony of colourful Atlantic puffins gregariously assembled on a rock outcropping.

Why, with excellent photographic equipment and skilled professional photographers available, are birds in field guides still drawn or painted? Why not use photographs? The answer is that a photograph shows the bird in one particular moment in time – posture, plumage, legs, and lighting all frozen in that instant. Seconds later a very different photograph could be taken. Painting or drawing captures the ideal posture and colour of a bird and draws attention to the features that are most important in identifying the species.

In addition to book illustrations, more people and organizations are buying and commissioning paintings with wildlife subjects. Hopefully it is because they appreciate wildlife and want to protect it; or perhaps they just want reminders of what it once was.

Arthur Singer

JANET TURNER
American, 1914–88

Janet Turner grew up on her family's Kansas farm, a time punctuated with summer camps at Cape Cod. Her sister Barbara noted that Janet was engrossed in every detail of the outdoors and believed that all of nature's creations were just as important as human beings. The natural world was at the forefront of her thinking. Even on her hospital deathbed, Turner said, "It's just nature's way".

Attending Stanford University in California, Turner was discouraged from majoring in biology because "it was not a field for women". So she majored in history, took courses in botany, and later enrolled in art classes. She started making prints with linocuts – similar to woodcuts but using a sheet of linoleum carved to create the design for printing. Receiving a degree in Far Eastern History and unable to find employment, she returned to Kansas and enrolled at the Kansas City Art Institute to study under Thomas Hart Benton. She taught for a year and then pursued her Master's of Fine Arts at Claremont College, studying with Millard Sheets.

Turner experimented with different forms and subjects of art, with birds as her main subjects. Her tempera painting *Pelicans* (see page 11) was chosen as part of an exhibition in American art at the Metropolitan Museum in New York. She continued to paint but eventually moved to serigraphy (silk-screen printing), as it seemed to be a less labour-intensive way to add colour to relief prints. Turner was elected to the Audubon Artists of New York and the National Association of Women Artists, and was a lifetime member of the National Academy of Design in New York. She then received an EdD from Columbia University and served as president of the National Serigraph Society.

Turner illustrated books and articles and sold prints, and in 1959 accepted a position in art education at California State University, Chico. Continuing to travel, teach, and produce prints, Turner eventually had 200 one-person shows, in 40 states and 50 countries on six continents.

After arriving in California, she began to concentrate on local bird images. She took hundreds of photographs and often borrowed bird skins from the university's natural history museum. Birds were the centrepiece of all of her works, and the backgrounds were faithful to the natural habitat. A pheasant, gingerly walking through a dense bed of live and dead reeds, hidden from prying eyes, looks up at a marsh wren peering down at him. Her magpie in a tree contrasts with the blossoms behind him. It appears that the tree was the main focus of the print and a magpie somehow got in the middle of it. In addition, two other magpies are surreptitiously flying in the distance, filling up the little space that the blossoms do not.

ABOVE: Janet Turner,
Black Vultures, 1950.

OPPOSITE: Janet Turner,
At the Nest of the Heron,
1953. This screenprint of
a blue heron is as much
about mood as it is about
the bird.

Her *Guinea Fowl* (1950, see page 172) and *Egg of the Flamingo* (1953) are examples of full-frame composition – the subjects fill the picture. Although the birds are realistic, their positions and interactions are not. The flamingo print, filled with more than a dozen flamingoes with their necks stretching in every direction, reminds one of a scene from *Alice in Wonderland*. They demonstrate her knowledge of Japanese woodcuts in their flat space.

The work she called *The Nightwatcher* (1955) is a print of a Great Horned Owl staring out at the viewer from behind a branch of autumn leaves with accusatory eyes. Perhaps her most dramatic work was that of *Wintering Snow Geese* (1968), which was an experiment combining linocuts with screen printing.

Turner's prints were all about mood. The atmosphere was often established with a heavy background and the bird or birds superimposed on it. In her *Cascade with Dippers* (1971), the rocks and the cascading waterfall are the whole picture, the dippers only a small part. That's perhaps what she was trying to impart to the viewer. In nature, you rarely see birds taking up the most space in your view – they are only a small part of the big picture.

TOP: Janet Turner, *Wintering Snow Geese*, 1968.

ABOVE: Janet Turner, *Chickens*, c.1948.

OPPOSITE: Janet Turner, *Beginning of Night*, 1962. Depicting a barn owl.

BIRD ART SUPPORTS BIRDS

ARTHUR B SINGER
American, 1917–90

Although Arthur Bernard Singer was born and raised in New York City, he developed a fascination for birds and spent a lot of time at the Bronx Zoo, developing his artistic talents for animal paintings. In 1939 he graduated from Cooper Union Art School and began work as an art teacher, director, and designer. Two years later some of his artwork was exhibited at the zoo.

After four years in the Army during the Second World War, he was commissioned to create eight prints of state birds and flowers for *American Home* magazine in 1956. The success of this publication resulted in several more contracts to paint birds. His reputation was made in 1961 with Oliver Austin's *Birds of the World* book, which contained over 700 of Singer's bird paintings, was published in eight languages, and sold hundreds of thousands of copies. This was followed, in 1966, with the field guide *Birds of North America*. In this guide Singer used numerous photographs of his own, supplemented by field sketches and skins, to perfect the plumage, eye and leg colour, and posture of each bird. He showed most of the ages, sexes, and seasonal plumages. He even spent some time at a bird-banding station in Maryland to compare his drawings to live handheld birds. He set the birds in their usual habitat, even placing a Northern Mockingbird on top of a TV antenna. This book competed with Roger Tory Peterson's bird guides (see page 168) in popularity; with over 6 million copies sold, it is the book for which Singer is best known.

Singer also illustrated *Families of Birds*, *Birds of Europe* (a field guide), and *Zoo Animals*. In 1973 he illustrated Alexander Skutch's *The Life of the Hummingbird*, painting brightly coloured hummingbirds in action poses larger than life. During the 1970s Singer travelled a good deal in search of birds he had never before seen. He illustrated the *Birds of the West Indies*, authored by James Bond. (This is the actual James Bond after whom Ian Fleming named his character; he was an ornithologist in the Caribbean.) Singer illustrated Bertel Bruun's *Birds of the Seven Continents*, but the death of the publisher ended the project.

In 1982 Singer and his son Alan painted a sheet of stamps depicting state birds and flowers for the US Postal Service; this became the biggest-selling single issue in US postal history, over 50 million sets. After that Singer devoted much of his time to painting on canvas and showing his artwork at galleries and museums. His work is still in demand.

Over his career Singer illustrated over 20 books and guides as well as making prints, painting on porcelain, and producing many watercolours and oils. He was a staunch advocate of habitat protection and was awarded with medals from the Cooper Ornithological Society and the National Audubon Society.

ABOVE: Arthur B Singer, *Eastern Bluebird and Rose*, 1982. The state bird and flower of New York depicted together.

OPPOSITE: Arthur B Singer, illustrations of woodpeckers for a field guide, date unknown.

OPPOSITE ABOVE: Arthur B Singer, *Ring-necked Pheasants in the Snow*, 1982.

OPPOSITE BELOW: Arthur B Singer, *Birds of the Seven Continents*, 1974 (rollers and bee-eaters).

RIGHT: Arthur B Singer's art on the cover of Alexander Skutch's *The Life of the Hummingbird* (1973).

KEITH SHACKLETON
British, 1923–2015

Keith Shackleton was an artist, illustrator, and naturalist best known for his large 60 by 90 cm (24 by 36 in) canvases of wildlife and landscapes, especially those of the Antarctic. He, like so many before him, emphasized that wildlife should be studied in the field. He said that photographs, field guides, films, study skins and museum mounts should be used only as supplementary resources, not primary ones. "It's wrong to get yourself involved in things you've never seen. Get out in the field."

ABOVE: Keith Shackleton, *On the Graham Coast: Snow Petrel*, 1984. Reveals the starkness of the environment.

OPPOSITE: Keith Shackleton, *Bermuda Petrel*, date unknown. Detailed bird over impressionistic landscape.

Shackleton, related to the famous explorer Sir Ernest Shackleton, became friends with the painter Peter Scott – son of Captain Robert Scott, who had led a party to the South Pole in 1912. He served five years with the Royal Air Force in Europe and the Far East during the Second World War, before returning to England to work in the family aviation business. He painted in his spare time, writing and illustrating two books. Then, in the 1960s, he became a co-host on a TV show about animals and later hosted his own children's wildlife series; he also decided to become a full-time painter.

Shackleton and Scott made several trips as members of a team of naturalists on the *Lindblad Explorer*, whose 1969 expeditionary cruise to Antarctica served as the predecessor of today's Antarctic tourism. His books and illustrations include *Birds of the Atlantic Ocean*, *A Sailor's Guide to Ocean Birds*, and *Wildlife and Wilderness*. In 2001 he published *Ship in the Wilderness: Voyages of the MS Explorer through the Last Wild Places on Earth*, in which he wrote about his passages through the Arctic, Antarctic, Atlantic, and Pacific. His meticulously done wildlife and marine paintings were dramatic and emotional, the foaming icy waters and bleak skies of the polar regions conveying a powerful impact.

He was active in the wildlife art community, serving as the president of the Society of Wildlife Artists and officer of several other art-oriented groups. Shackleton also worked with the Royal Society for the Protection of Birds' Save the Albatross campaign and was a founding member of Peter Scott's Wildfowl Trust. He was awarded Member of the Most Excellent Order of the British Empire for his work in conservation.

Keith Shackleton aimed for "an exciting painting with a wildlife dimension", perhaps exaggerating to emphasize a point. Shackleton said that there is often a conflict between painting an animal in a finely detailed way to reflect reality and that of artistic interpretation. A photograph may be perfectly realistic, but in painting every detail, every feather, every colour that a photograph shows, there is the danger of losing the sense of vitality and originality. The setting of the animal,

the landscape, provides the mood of the painting. Therefore, Shackleton paints in the subject and then builds the background around it, taking care to scale it correctly. His snow petrel and snow geese paintings beautifully illustrate these points.

ABOVE: Keith Shackleton, *Rough Seas with Albatross in Flight*, 1977.

OPPOSITE ABOVE: Keith Shackleton, *Snow Geese*, 1957. There is a keen sense of movement and energy.

OPPOSITE BELOW: Keith Shackleton, *Avocets Working the Shallows, Havergate Island*, 1968. Havergate Island is a marshy nature reserve in England run by the Royal Society for the Protection of Birds.

BIRD ART SUPPORTS BIRDS

BIRD ART SUPPORTS BIRDS

WILLIAM THOMAS COOPER
Australian, 1934–2015

Wildlife illustrator William T Cooper was deemed one of the greatest of all bird artists by BBC TV naturalist Sir David Attenborough. Attenborough said he believed Cooper was "Australia's greatest living scientific painter of birds"; perhaps "the best in the world". Sir David went on to make a TV documentary about Cooper, called Portrait Painter to the Birds, *in 1993.*

For many years, ornithologists tended to lean either towards systematics (naming and classifying) or towards natural history, later ecology. By the middle of the twentieth century, these two camps had mostly merged. Bird artists, though, stayed with natural history, simply because that is what they needed to form a mental image of the birds they were painting. The birds' habitat, food, nest sites, predators, and behaviour are what matters, not their relationships or names. Although Cooper's paintings are so good that the relationships of some birds to others can be easily seen, that was not his goal. His aim was simply to paint these spectacular birds in the way that they deserve to be seen.

Cooper grew up in Newcastle, a poor New South Wales suburb, in the depression of the 1930s. His family lived in a small shack, but Cooper found his way to the Cary Bay Zoo, where he learned taxidermy. He was fascinated by the works of the famous John Gould, who, with his wife Elizabeth (see page 96), illustrated *Birds of Australia*. Cooper started his art career by painting commercial landscapes and seascapes while working as a window dresser and a clothing store salesman. In the 1950s he painted murals for hotels and private homes; unfortunately, most of these art works have since disappeared.

Cooper's career as a commercial artist faded as he gathered fame for his natural history and scientific illustrations, especially of birds. The first book he illustrated, written by ornithologist Keith Hindwood in 1967, was *Portfolio of Australian Birds*. A review of his work in an American journal noted that the paintings are "exceptionally well drawn and well composed, forceful and inventive". A similar review said, "Cooper's paintings are superb in every respect." Then in April 1970, Cooper made his first trip out of Australia to paint Papua New Guinea's more unusual parrots. He illustrated *Parrots of the World*, *The Birds of Paradise and Bower Birds*, *Australian Parrots*, and the *Cockatoos and Turacos*, all written by parrot expert Joseph Forshaw. Cooper also illustrated *Visions of a Rainforest* by Stanley Breeden and *Fruits of the Australian Tropical Rainforest* by his wife, Wendy Cooper. In addition, the government of Papua New Guinea commissioned him to illustrate two sets of postage stamps.

ABOVE: William T Cooper, *Rainbows on the Moor*, 2012. Rainbow lorikeets feeding from the flowers of the grass tree in the morning sun.

OPPOSITE: William T Cooper, *Red-tailed Black Cockatoos*, 2013. Male watching female resting in a weeping melaleuca tree beside the Walsh River in north Queensland.

Cooper painted birds using watercolours, with detailed precision, and he usually did so in the field. He preferred to draw from life and so ventured into the wild to capture the poses and behaviours of birds, even noting the food they ate. A stickler for detail, he was once caught in the bush without his sketchbook when a White-Quilled Rock Pigeon landed in a nearby bush. Not wanting to forget the details of the bird's posture and plumage, he took out a felt pen and scratched out a sketch on the brim of his hat.

In 1992 he was awarded the Gold Medal of the American Academy of Natural Sciences for distinction in natural history art, the first Australian recipient of the award in the 190-year history of the Academy. In 1994 he was awarded the Order of Australia for contributions to art and ornithology.

ABOVE: William T Cooper, *Blue Bird of Paradise*, 1991. The inverted courtship display of the blue bird of paradise is depicted against a backdrop of the rainforest of New Guinea.

OPPOSITE ABOVE: William T Cooper, *Australian Shelducks*, 2001. Cooper stated: "I was inspired by being able to sit quite close to a pair in Kings Park in Perth WA where I could study the beauty of their plumage".

OPPOSITE BELOW: William T Cooper, *Kookaburras*, 2004. The laughing kookaburra is the world's largest kingfisher and probably vies with the emu for the title of the most popular Australian bird.

JAMES FENWICK LANSDOWNE
Canadian, 1937–2008

Lansdowne's detailed watercolours of birds are reminiscent of the work of John James Audubon (see page 86), typically featuring a particular bird against a minimal background of mostly white. However, Lansdowne's paintings are much more natural and lifelike than those of Audubon.

ABOVE: James Fenwick Lansdowne, *Eurasian Bullfinch*, 1983.

OPPOSITE: James Fenwick Lansdowne, *Sharp-shinned Hawk*, 2000. The bird is featured with prey, and shows exquisite details of feather texture and position.

Born in Hong Kong to British parents and raised in Victoria, British Columbia, Lansdowne became an avid birdwatcher at the age of 12, despite being partially handicapped by a bout of polio. Largely self-taught as an artist (although influenced by his mother, who was trained in traditional Chinese watercolour techniques), he had his first show at the Royal Ontario Museum in 1956, when he was only 19. Since then he has exhibited around the world.

In 1966, *Birds of the Northern Forest* was published, co-authored by Lansdowne and John Livingston. George Miksch Sutton, renowned bird artist, reviewed the book, saying "Lansdowne is a talented young man whose bird portraiture ... is charming and authentic." In Sutton's review of *Birds of the Eastern Forest Vol II*, again created with Livingston, Sutton guesses that Lansdowne had studied earlier artists who drew the same species, but he notes that Lansdowne has developed his own style. Sutton applauds Lansdowne for the excellent composition of each plate, a skill that is hard to learn and apply, as Lansdowne selected each and every berry, twig, and leaf with care and positioned them exactly where they belong.

Lansdowne illustrated *Rails of the World* by Dillon Ripley in 1977 and *Guide to the Behavior of Common Birds* with Donald Stokes in 1980.

In 1984, he was commissioned to paint *Rare Birds of China*, which took ten years to complete because he had to travel across the country, visiting zoos, museums, and observing birds in the wild. The 32 birds were printed in 100-print sets, signed by Lansdowne.

Working in watercolours with a minimal white or off-white background, Lansdowne created paintings that seem more thought-provoking than dramatic. Comparing Audubon's *Common Nighthawk* painting with that of Lansdowne's, for example, Audubon's two birds seem ungainly, awkward, and more hawk-like than nighthawk-like, while Lansdowne's single bird elegantly and effortlessly pursues its prey. Lansdowne also notes on his work the exact museum specimen that he studied, but it is clear that he had to have made long observations of live birds in their aerial pursuits to paint such an expressive picture.

Unlike contemporaries such as Shackleton and Singer, who installed their subjects on a moderate or full landscape, Lansdowne kept his backgrounds much simpler – a twig, a few leaves, a stump, or just water, not unlike Elizabeth Gould, Alexander Wilson, and George Edwards (see pages 96, 76 and 52 respectively) of a couple of centuries ago. Like other artists of his time, Lansdowne was influenced

J.F. Lansdowne
· 2000 ·

early by Fuertes, Audubon and Thorburn (see pages 140, 86 and 128 respectively). It's possible that later in life, Lansdowne was inspired by Edward Lear and Joseph Wolf (see pages 106 and 110). Indeed, some of the pheasant paintings by Lansdowne in *Rare Birds of China* are decidedly reminiscent of the Wolf style.

Lansdowne's work has been presented to members of the British Royal Family by the Government of Canada. In 1974, he was elected a member of the Royal Canadian Academy of Arts. In 1976, he was made an Officer of the Order of Canada, the award stating "Ornithological artist of wide renown, with the rare ability not only to be essentially correct in his paintings of birds, but to portray them so they seemingly come to life."

In 1995, he was awarded the Order of British Columbia.

ABOVE LEFT: James Fenwick Lansdowne, *Pygmy Owl*, 1990 – with unusually large prey.

ABOVE RIGHT: James Fenwick Lansdowne, *Bare-eyed Rail*, date unknown.

OPPOSITE: James Fenwick Lansdowne, *Impeyan Monal*, from *Rare Birds of China* (1998).

Chapter Ten

ORNITHOLOGICAL
ART EXPANDS

———

By the latter part of the twentieth century, bird field guides were common, new ones continually being published, and the birdwatching hobby ever expanding. Anyone who was interested could identify common birds with only a little effort. Numerous other books were published in which the focus was not identification but the pleasure of the illustrations. Books with titles such as *The World of Birds, Birds of the World*, and the *Encyclopedia of Birds* were popular, partly for their information but mostly because of their large, colourful pictures with birds in interesting postures and habitats.

Perhaps the most ambitious set of books is the 17-volume series *Handbook of Birds of the World*, which Hilary Burn had a hand in illustrating. An encyclopedic reference rather than a field guide, it illustrates in paintings and photographs every species of bird in the world. Each book is a hefty tome, but very attractive and enlightening.

In addition to books, there are prints, watercolours, oil paintings, etchings, sculptures, carvings, and other artwork of birds. Some are especially realistic, almost photographic, as are some of the works of Lars Jonsson and Elizabeth Butterworth. On the other hand there are artworks done by the likes of Raymond Harris-Ching, whose watercolours range from exquisite realism to imaginative to bizarre.

In days past, birds were considered both symbols and predictors of events. As noted in the introduction, doves are symbols of love and peace, owls of wisdom, storks bring babies and good luck, and ravens predict death. Swans symbolized purity and vultures epitomized greed. Today those symbols are not as meaningful as they once were although some birds still retain an aura of symbolism. Mostly, birds are our most apparent connection to nature. Their songs, their colours, their freedom in the air, and their ubiquity constantly remind us that there is a world external to the everyday one we live in.

Today bird art is not so much symbolic as simply attractive. Some bird art reminds us of our wonderful world of nature. Other art evokes emotion. Most works are just plain enjoyable, no matter what medium is used or what birds they depict. Artists and their creations are as varied as birds.

PREVIOUS PAGE: Elizabeth Butterworth, *Buzzard's Wings*, 2010–13. Showing the underside and upperside.

OPPOSITE: Lars Jonsson, *Arctic Patterns*, 2008. Depicting a gyrfalcon in a snowy landscape.

RAYMOND HARRIS-CHING

New Zealand, 1939–

*Raymond Ching had an early start. Dropping out of his
Wellington, New Zealand, high school at the age of just 12, he
somehow secured a job as an apprentice in an advertising firm.
He moved his way up to art director, but then, remembering his
fascination with birds after a museum visit, he started painting
watercolours, displayed his works, and sold paintings. His first
major exhibition in Auckland in 1966 was a huge success.*

Sir William Collins of Collins Publishing, a Scottish publisher and an avid
ornithologist, discovered Ching at his second exhibition and convinced
him to move to London. Collins and *Reader's Digest* wanted to do a major
field guide on the birds of Britain but had not been able to find a suitable artist –
until Harris-Ching. The publishers figured that it would take six artists a year to
illustrate *The Reader's Digest Book of British Birds*. Ching promised to do it himself
in one year, and he did, producing 230 full-colour pictures and exhausting himself
in the process. Published in 1969, the book was in print for over 40 years through
many editions and in ten languages. It was the world's best-selling bird book.

He went on to publish a dozen books, including *Raymond Ching, The Bird Paintings, Watercolours and Pencil Drawings* (1969–75), *The Art of Raymond Ching* (1981), *New Zealand Birds: An Artist's Field Studies* (1986), and others. In 1999 he designed a British first-class stamp titled *Darwin's Theory*, in which a bird stands next to a fossil of *Archaeopteryx*, the first bird.

Ching continued to paint in both oils and watercolours. His art has been described as conservative realism; many images project a photographic quality, although he may leave out details of the landscape. Unusually for most bird artists of the past few hundred years, Ching has not spent much time observing birds in the field; he prefers cities.

His styles and content vary considerably, sometimes pushing the boundaries of bird art by blending imagination with realism and occasionally adding human figures to his bird portraits. They range from the realistic to the obscure to the bizarre. In *The Hawk, The Falcon and the Pigeons*, in which a hawk plucks an individual from a flock of pigeons, terrifying all the other pigeons, there is almost photographic realism. In *News Travelled Quickly,* two birds, hardly visible, announce with word balloons someone's arrival at a shack in a very realistic tropical forest edge. In *First Time Away*, a black swan with three cygnets reflects an impressionistic style. *Tarapunga and the Gulls* shows the aggressive postures of two black-backed gulls towards a red-billed gull (*tarapunga* in Maori language), while a crab ponders a move to a quieter place inland. The picture includes a cursive explanation at the bottom. In 2006 he painted *Learning to Fly in the Funny Pages* in which a toucan and a young woman float over a background of newspaper comics with empty word balloons over their heads. Another illegible cursive explanation lurks in the corner. Although his naturalistic paintings have given way to more impressionistic and imaginary ones, birds continue to be a major feature. In the process, Harris-Ching has transformed himself from a field guide illustrator to a free-flowing artist, and he has achieved great success in his field.

Hilary Burn.

HILARY BURN
British, 1946–

A very productive bird artist but one of the least known, Hilary Burn stands out in a male-dominated field. She has been the primary illustrator in 11 books and shared the duties with others in many more. She considers herself a scientist, an ornithologist with artistic talent, rather than an artist with an interest in birds. Her father was a draughtsman and her great uncle an art teacher. She is also a birder – but not a twitcher, she says – and learned how to ring (band) birds.

Hilary Burn received a degree in zoology at Leeds University and taught for two years in a comprehensive school in Leeds. Her now ex-husband encouraged her to paint birds and took her to her first British Trust for Ornithology meeting. There she happened to meet Robert Gillmor, ornithologist, artist, and a founder of the Society of Wildlife Artists.

She began her professional career in art by illustrating *Woodlice*, a book written by one of her lecturers at Leeds. Next came *Drosophila* and then *Aphids*, but most illustrations after those were birds and occasionally mammals.

Burn's paintings are careful and detailed, and put as much emphasis on habitat as on the birds' form and plumage. A review of her illustrations in *Wildfowl of Europe* notes that her birds are "extremely lifelike and attractive". She illustrated *Crows and Jays: A Guide to the Crows, Jays, and Magpies of the World* with 122 paintings. Glen Woolfenden, renowned ornithologist and expert on jays, said that he looked at 90 illustrations of *Corvus* (genus of crows) and could easily pick out the American Crow because of Burn's meticulous artwork. Woolfenden said, "I applaud Burn."

A reviewer of *An Identification Guide to the Ducks, Geese, and Swans of the World* said that her "illustrations are bright, colourful, and distinctly rendered for identification while being quite detailed and artistic." "Overall the best collection of waterfowl painting in a guide book." Critical of her own work, she says that "getting it right" means that it feels as if the bird is lying on the paper and she is painting on top of the feathers. She is an admirer of bird artists Archibald Thorburn (see page 128), Eric Ennion (see page 164), Robert Gillmor, and Canadian artist Robert Bateman.

Burn painted for *The Handbook of Bird Identification for Europe and the Western Palearctic* (1998) and co-illustrated the *Guide to the Birds of Southeast Asia* (2000). From 1992 to 2011, she worked with several other artists to produce the 17-volume series *Handbook of Birds of the World*, which illustrates both in drawings and photographs every bird in the world. Her paintings are careful, articulate, and scientific, with emphasis on "jizz" – the overall impression of the bird and its posture, behaviour, and habitat. She says she paints for people who love birds and not for the opinions of the art world.

TOP: Hilary Burn, *Wigeon Male and Female and Young*, from *Wildfowl of Europe* (1977).

ABOVE: Hilary Burn, *Mandarin Ducks with Young*, from *Wildfowl of Europe*.

OPPOSITE: Hilary Burn, *Common Goldeneye with Young*, from *Wildfowl of Europe*.

LEFT: Hilary Burn,
*Eider duck, Male
and Female, with
Ducklings,* from
Wildfowl of Europe.

RIGHT: Hilary
Burn, *Canada
Geese*, from
*Wildfowl of
Europe*.

ELIZABETH BUTTERWORTH
British, 1949–

Parrots have always been admired for their colours, their exotic bearings, their tameness, and their ability to be trained to mimic human sounds. Today we find them just as interesting.

In 1436 Jan van Eyck painted a Madonna and Child with a ring-necked parakeet. In 1533 a similar painting by Hans Baldung contains a grey parrot. Then there are Melchior d'Hondecoeter's *Menagerie* with several parrots in 1690 and Tiepolo's *Woman with a Parrot* in 1761. Perhaps the most well known of parrot painters is Edward Lear (see page 106) who produced 42 hand-coloured lithographs entitled *Parrots*. Lear, unlike most previous artists, made his drawings from live specimens.

Today we have Elizabeth Butterworth, one of the best artists at capturing the bright plumage of macaws. She watched them in their native tropical habitats in South America and raised them in her back garden in England. She has examined the skins of parrots in museums in London and New York.

Elizabeth Butterworth was born in England and studied locally at the Rochdale School of Art in Greater Manchester, then the Maidstone School of Art, before completing her training at the Royal College of Art in London. She had her first solo show in London in 1975, then exhibited at several venues, including New York, Tokyo, Caracas, and Adelaide, as well as participating in a number of group exhibitions in Europe and the United States. In addition to her watercolours, she produces prints; her work was featured in the portfolios *Parrots and Cockatoos* (1978), *Amazon Parrots* (1983), and *Macaws* (1993).

Butterworth often paints from life in the field in South America and in her own parrot menagerie. Her work is in the tradition of John Gould and Archibald Thorburn who were ornithologists as well as artists, but her work seems closer to that of Edward Lear, who was more of an artist than scientist. Her realistic depictions of parrots have been described as having a "surreal or super-real quality". The art historian and critic, Ian Dunlop, noted in 1993 that Butterworth is "without rival this century". Richard Verdi, author of *The Parrot in Art: From Durer to Elizabeth Butterworth* (2007), describes her as "the greatest parrot illustrator of our time". Mark Fisher, of the British newsmagazine *The Spectator*, writes that Butterworth's "technique is immaculate ... she is a superb colourist ... poised between scientific recording and imaginative art".

Not only adept at picturing whole birds, she paints parts of them as well. A Lear's macaw painting shows the head of the bird as well as two feathers in exquisite detail. A palm cockatoo painting shows an unfinished head alongside a complete one and a feather; again, wonderful detail. A sulphur-crested cockatoo pencil sketch alongside a detailed head is a nice contrast. And more than a few

ABOVE: Elizabeth Butterworth, *Sulphur-crested Cockatoo Head with Pencil Sketch*, c.1980s.

OPPOSITE: Elizabeth Butterworth, *Yellow-tailed Black Cockatoo*, 2008.

are just a wing, created with photographic realism. Her birds are realistic, but the detail of the feathers of the individual wings or tail just explodes off the page.

Her works are held in over 25 institutions, including libraries, museums, art galleries, and university collections all over the world: England, the United States, Australia, Germany, Canada, Venezuela, and South Africa.

ORNITHOLOGICAL ART EXPANDS

LARS JONSSON
Swedish, 1952–

Lars Jonsson, ornithologist and bird artist, started painting birds when he was four. At seven years his parents entered him into an art contest, only to be accused of fraud as "someone so young could not have painted like young Jonsson".

At 15, he exhibited his paintings at the Swedish Museum of Natural History in Stockholm. In the late 1970s he wrote and illustrated a series of six bird guides including *Birds of Sea and Coast* and *Birds of Mountain Regions*. In 1999 he published a five-volume work, *Birds of Europe: With North Africa and the Middle East*, later translated into several languages and becoming an essential resource for any European birder. Some have described Jonsson as the "greatest living bird artist".

Jonsson's work has been compared to that of Bruno Liljefors (see page 132), whom he acknowledges as an influence, and Louis Agassiz Fuertes (see page 140). However, Jonsson is self-taught; his artistic ability is innate and was perfected with practice. His styles vary from near photographic to watercolours that are more impressionistic. Since oil paints can be reworked a bit over time because oil takes some time to dry, they look more finished, while his watercolours look more spontaneous.

OPPOSITE: Lars Jonsson, *Common Shelducks*, 1994. Gravånder ducks (shelducks) facing the viewer; a very unusual composition.

BELOW: Lars Jonsson, *Rook*, from his *Winter Birds* (2017). "Their featherless face adds a human characteristic and when seen from the front it resembles an old woman with a black head-scarf"– Jonsson.

RIGHT: Lars Jonsson, *Raven Winter*, 2010. Very true to life.

OPPOSITE: Lars Jonsson, *In the Evening*, 1998. A photorealistic lithograph of a pied avocet.

Like many before him, Jonsson spends a considerable amount of time in the field, using a telescope as much as a pencil or brush. He draws from life, usually from a distance, using a spotting telescope. This works well with birds like hawks, that brazenly sit in a broad landscape, such as his gyrfalcon (see page 199). Rarely does he show songbirds in the brush or trees, as they are wont to disappear quickly. He sketches with pencil so confidently that he never erases. At times he paints or uses pen and ink without an initial pencil sketch. One advantage that he has over earlier painters is using high-speed photography that shows the birds in motion. Never copying a photograph, Jonsson must have used several to remind him of what birds looked like in flight.

As Jonsson explains, "I feel a strong primitive attraction towards painting, towards creating a feeling of truth… it is faithfulness to nature that I am seeking." In his *Common Shelducks* painting, three of the five ducks look out of the painting, giving the viewer a full frontal of the ducks' faces. Ducks face each other all the time, but rarely do they look at us from a painting. But this is the way it is in nature. *In the Evening* shows the a pied avocet with young, the birds in superbly realistic against a somewhat impressionistic background of sky and water.

Jonsson's works are in several art collections, including the National Museum of Wildlife Art in Jackson Hole, Wyoming. The museum's director, Adam Harris, writes, "To even attempt to capture the beauty of nature … requires more thought, more time, more energy than most artists are willing to invest, but, to Jonsson, this investment is part and parcel of what it means to be an artist."

Birds and Light: the Art of Lars Jonsson is part autobiography and part a description of the author's methods, illustrated with his artwork, including sketchbooks, and covering the development and completion of finished canvases.

Where Heaven and Earth Touch: The Art of Birdpainter Lars Jonsson, another book on Jonsson's art, was published in conjunction with the first exhibition of his work in the Federal Republic of Germany. In 2009 he published *Lars Jonsson's Birds: Paintings from a Near Horizon*, featuring 150 full-colour, museum-quality reproductions of works painted in the field. Douglas Pratt, ornithologist and painter, in his review of that work, writes that Jonsson has the innate ability and has done the work to become perhaps the premier bird artist of our time.

His latest book is *Winter Birds* (2017).

1/310

DAVID ALLEN SIBLEY
American, 1961–

First there was John James Audubon (see page 86), then Roger Tory Peterson (see page 168), and today we have David Allen Sibley. The son of ornithologist Fred Sibley, David began birdwatching early. He was accepted into the prestigious ornithology programme at Cornell University, New York, but quit after one year, instead travelling across North America, watching and drawing birds.

L eading birdwatching tours in the 1980s and 1990s, he was disappointed by the available field guides because they did not show all the plumages that a bird might have. So, as a self-taught artist, Sibley published his first bird field guide in 2000, *The Sibley Guide to Birds*, and the birdwatching community quickly began to use the name Sibley as a synonym for field guide. This is by far the most detailed and complete bird field guide ever published in the United States. Including 810 species illustrated in 6,600 detailed paintings depicting male, female, immature, summer and winter plumages, the book was an immense undertaking. The second edition, published in 2014 included 600 totally new images and 111 new species. An example is his blackpoll and bay-breasted warbler drawings, 16 on the page, showing various plumages.

Sibley created all the images first in pencil and then in gouache paints. It took about six years to produce, following six years of planning. If there was any complaint among birdwatchers about the book, it was the size: too big and heavy for a field guide. He later published eastern and western North America guides that were smaller, and, with fewer pages, easier to carry.

Following his first field guide came eight other books, mostly field guides to birds, but also a field guide to trees, a book about bird behaviour, and an illustrated anthology of poems about birds. He has also illustrated a number of other books such as the *Atlas of Breeding Birds in New York State* (1988) and *Tales of a Low-Rent Birder* (1986).

Sibley used to take photos of birds but says, like so many other artists, that fieldwork is most important. He spends a lot of time outside studying how feather patterns merge to create an overall pattern and how those patterns fit around the bird. He paints the originals about three times the size of the printed version, so sometimes the paintings are larger than life. The hardest part is the feet, he says.

In his early years, Sibley was most influenced by Arthur Singer's *Birds of the World* (see page 180) and studied his paintings as well as those of Louis Agassiz Fuertes (see page 140) and especially Lars Jonsson (see page 210). His tree swallows resemble Jonsson's work, the phoebe is perhaps reminiscent of Singer, and the snowy owl that of Fuertes.

ABOVE: David Allen Sibley, *Pair of Tree Swallows*, 2014.

OPPOSITE: David Allen Sibley, *Snowy Owl*, 2011.

DAS 2011

ABOVE: David Allen Sibley, blackpoll (left) and bay-breasted (right) warblers as they appear in *The Sibley Guide to Birds* (2000).

OPPOSITE ABOVE: David Allen Sibley, *Black Phoebe Singing*, 2015.

OPPOSITE BELOW: David Allen Sibley, *Bewick's Wren*, 2015.

Sibley's bird guide is art, but in a very practical sense. The birds, all facing to the right in a stiff-legged or frozen-in-flight posture, are practical rather than decorative artworks. His paintings are admirable for their detailed description of a particular species; the artwork is perfection and the field guide probably the best that has ever been published – like a dictionary defines words, Sibley defines birds. Although not placed in context, the paintings are extremely useful for reference. They demonstrate that representational artwork based on painstaking, accurate observation still has a vitally important role in conveying information about birds.

DAS 2015

DAS 2015

BIBLIOGRAPHY

Allen, E. "The History of American Ornithology before Audubon." *Transactions of the American Philosophical Society* 41, no. 3 (1951): 387–591.

Allen, Elsa G. "New Light on Mark Catesby." *The Auk: Ornithological Advances* 54, no. 3 (Jul 1937): 349–363.

Ashley, M. "Elizabeth Gould." John Gould: Bird Illustration in the Age of Darwin (internet; 2019). https://exhibits.lib.ku.edu/exhibits/show/gould/about/elizabeth_gould

Baetjer, Katharine. "British Portraits in The Metropolitan Museum of Art." *Metropolitan Museum of Art Bulletin* 57, no. 1 (Summer 1999): 1–72.

Bailey, Florence Merriam. *Handbook of Birds of the Western United States: Including the Great Plains, Great Basin, Pacific Slope, and Lower Rio Grande Valley.* Boston and New York: Houghton Mifflin, 1902.

Berger, A. "George Miksch Sutton." *The Wilson Bulletin* 80, no. 1 (1968): 30–35.

Bewick, Thomas. *A General History of the Quadrupeds.* Printed by Edward Walker, 1811.

Birkhead, Timothy, Jo Wimpenny, and Bob Montgomery. *Ten Thousand Birds: Ornithology Since Darwin.* Princeton, NJ: Princeton University Press, 2014.

Blauvelt, H. "Bruno Liljefors – Greatest of Wildlife Painters." *The American Magazine of Art.* 17, no. 10 (1926): 505–512.

Bonta, Marcia. "Graceanna Lewis: Portrait of a Quaker Naturalist." *Quaker History* 74, no. 1 (Spring 1985): 27–40.

Boreman, Thomas. *A Description of Three Hundred Animals ... with a Particular Account of the Manner of Their Catching of Whales in Greenland.* Printed for H. Woodfall, 1773.

Bridson, Gavin D. R. "From Xylography to Holography: Five Centuries of Natural History Illustration." *Archives of Natural History* 16, no. 2 (1989): 121–141.

Burtt, Edward H., and William E. Davis. *Alexander Wilson: the Scot Who Founded American Ornithology.* Cambridge, MA: Harvard University Press, 2013.

Butterworth, Elizabeth. "Feather artworks" (internet; 2019). https://featherartworks.org/pages/elizabeth_butterworth

Carlson, Douglas. *Roger Tory Peterson: A Biography.* Austin, TX: University of Texas Press, 2007.

Catesby, M. "Of Birds of Passage, by Mr. Mark Catesby, F. R. S." *Philosophical Transactions of the Royal Society of London* 44, no. 478–484 (Jan 1746): 435–444.

Chansigaud, V. *All About Birds: A Short Illustrated History of Ornithology.* Princeton, NJ: Princeton University Press, 2010.

Chisholm, A.H. *The Story of Elizabeth Gould.* Melbourne, Australia: Hawthorne Press, 1944.

Cocker, Mark, and David Tipling. *Birds and People.* London: Random House, 2013.

Decoen, Jean. "Carel Fabritius." *The Burlington Magazine* 69, no. 401 (Aug 1936): 52–55, 58–59.

Drennen, Susan Roney. "In Memoriam: Roger Tory Peterson, 1908–1996." *The Auk: Ornithological Advances* 115, no. 2 (Apr 1998): 465–469.

Duparc, Frederik J. "Results of the Recent Art-Historical and Technical Research on Carel Fabritius's Early Work." *Oud Holland* 119, no. 2/3 (2006): 76–89.

Edwards, George. *A Natural History of Uncommon Birds and of Some Other Rare and Undescribed Animals.* London: College of Physicians, 1743.

Ehrlich, Paul R., David S. Dobkin and Darryl Wheye. *The Birder's Handbook: a Field Guide to the Natural History of North American Birds.* New York: Simon and Schuster, 1988.

Elphick, Jonathan. *Birds: the Art of Ornithology.* New York: Skira Rizzoli Publications, 2017.

Estate of Arthur Singer. "Arthur Singer" (internet; 2017). http://singerarts.com/arthur/

Farber, P. "The Development of Taxidermy and the History of Ornithology." *Isis* 68, no. 4 (1977): 550–566.

Fisher, Clemency Thorne. "Wolf, Joseph (1820–1899)." *Oxford Dictionary of National Biography.* Oxford, UK: Oxford University Press, 2004.

Flis, Nathan. "The Drawings of Francis Barlow: From Apprenticeship to Aesop's Fables, 1648–66." *Master Drawings* 49, no. 4 (2011): 479–532.

Friedmann, H. *The symbolic goldfinch: its history and significance in European devotional art.* Washington, DC: Pantheon Books, 1946.

Frith, Clifford B. *Charles Darwin's Life with Birds: His Complete Ornithology.* New York: Oxford University Press, 2016.

"G." "Three Dutch Pictures." *Museum of Fine Arts Bulletin* 5, no. 29 (1907): 57–58.

Gerdts, William H. "The Influence of Ruskin and Pre-Raphaelitism on American Still-Life Painting." *American Art Journal* 1, no. 2 (1969): 80–97.

Gillispie, Charles C, Frederic L. Holmes, Noretta Koertge, et al (eds). Alexander Wilson. In: *Complete Dictionary of Scientific Biography.* Detroit, MI; Charles Scribner's Sons, 2008.

Goddeeris, Boudewijn, et al. "Some Gastronomic Aspects of Bird Species in Still Life Paintings of Frans Snyders (Antwerp, 1579-1657)." *Revue Belge De Philologie Et D'histoire* 80, no. 4 (2002): 1431–1448.

Goldi, John. "Major Allan Brooks DSO (1869-1945) & John Goldi Csc – A Boy & His Hero." theCanadaSite.com (internet; 2019). http://thecanadasite.com/art/art55_brooks.html

Graves, Robert Edmund (ed.). *Bryan's Dictionary of Painters and Engravers (A–K).* Vol. I (3rd ed.). London: George Bell & Sons, 1886.

Harm, Ray. "Creative Fine Art… is it or isn't it? Fine art vs. the tracing and copying of photos." Ray Harm Comments on Art (internet; 2019). https://rayharm.com/comm.html .

Harris, H. "Examples of Recent American Bird Art." *The Condor* 28, no. 5 (1926): 191–206.

Harris-Ching, Raymond, and Errol Fuller. *Studies and Sketches of a Bird Painter.* Melbourne, Australia: Lansdowne Editions, 1981.

Hindwood, K A. "The Late Neville W. Cayley: An Appreciation." *Emu – Austral Ornithology* 50, no. 1 (1950): 52–56.

Hindwood, Keith. Mrs. John Gould. *Emu – Austral Ornithology* 38, no. 2 (1938): 137–138.

Hulme, Frederick Edward. *Myth-Land.* London: Sampson Low, Marston, Searle, & Rivington, 1886.

Jackson, Christine E. "The Changing Relationship between J. J. Audubon and His Friends P. J. Selby, Sir William Jardine and W. H. Lizars." *Archives of Natural History* 18, no. 3 (1991): 289–307.

Jackson, Christine E. "W Hart – John Gould's Second Unknown Bird Artist." *Archives of Natural History* 14, no. 3 (1987): 237–241.

Jackson, Jerome A. "An Eye for Birds – The Life of George Miksch Sutton." Sutton

Center (internet; 2018). https://www.suttoncenter.org/about/history/the-life-of-george-miksch-sutton/

Kear, Janet. "Review – Prideaux John Selby: A Gentleman Naturalist, by Christine E. Jackson." *The Quarterly Review of Biology* 70, no. 3 (1995): 326.

Laing, Hamilton M. "Allan Brooks, 1896–1946." *The Auk: Ornithological Advances* 64, no. 3 (Jul 1947): 430–444.

Lambourne, Maureen. *John Gould: Bird Man*. London: Royal Society for Nature Conservation, 1987.

Lansdowne, J. Fenwick, and Nicholas Tuele. *Fenwick Lansdowne: Rare Birds of China*. Victoria, BC: Art Gallery of Greater Victoria, 1998.

Levi, Peter. *Edward Lear: a Life*. London: Tauris Parke Paperbacks, 2013.

Mason, A. Stuart. *George Edwards: the Bedell and His Birds*. London: Royal College of Physicians, 1992.

Mathews, Gregory. "Obituary: The Late John Gerrard Keulemans." *British Birds* Jul 1912:58.

Mattingley, Christobel. "Birds of a feather." *National Library of Australia News* 13, no. 7 (Apr 2003): 3–6.

McBurney, H. "The Parrot in Art: From Dürer to Elizabeth Butterworth." *The Burlington Magazine* 149, no. 1253 (2007): 560.

Meyers, Amy R. W, and Margaret Beck Pritchard. *Empire's Nature: Mark Catesby's New World Vision*. Chapel Hill, NC: University of North Carolina Press, 1998.

Neu, John. "Current Bibliography of the History of Science and Its Cultural Influences, 1989." *Isis* 80 (1989): 1–256.

Oakley, Howard. "No Greater Naturalist: Paintings of Bruno Liljefors, 1." The Eclectic Light Company (internet; 3 Mar 2018). https://eclecticlight.co/2018/03/03/no-greater-naturalist-paintings-of-bruno-liljefors-1/

O'Connell, K. "Review: Dictionary of Bird Artists of the World, Christine E. Jackson." *Art Documentation: Journal of the Art Libraries Society of North America* 19, no. 1 (2000): 54–55.

Ord, George. *American ornithology; or, The natural history of the birds of the United States. By Alexander Wilson. With a sketch of the author's life*. New York: Collins & Co., 1818–1829.

Palmer, A. H. *The life of Joseph Wolf*. London and New York: Longmans, Green and Co., 1895.

Peck, R. M. *A Celebration of Birds: The Life and Art of Louis Agassiz Fuertes. Published for the Academy of Natural Sciences of Philadelphia*. London: Collins, 1983.

Pettingill, Olin Sewall, Jr. "In Memoriam: George Miksch Sutton." *The Auk: Ornithological Advances* 101, no. 1 (Jan 1984): 146–152.

Pratt, H. Douglas. "Lars Jonsson's Birds: Paintings from a Near Horizon." *The Auk: Ornithological Advances* 127, no. 3 (Jul 2010): 721–724.

Raikow, R. "Review: Wildfowl of Europe, by Myrfyn Owen." *The Wilson Bulletin* 90, no. 1 (Mar 1978): 150–151.

Robbins, C. "In Memoriam: Arthur Bernard Singer, 1917–1990." *The Auk: Ornithological Advances* 110, no. 2 (Apr 1993): 376–377.

Roger Tory Peterson Institute. "Biography." The Roger Tory Peterson Institute of Natural History (internet; 2019). https://rtpi.org/roger-tory-peterson/roger-tory-peterson-biography/

Rose, Hugh James. *A New General Biographical Dictionary, Volume 6*. Charleston, SC: Nabu Press, 2011.

Ruskin, John. *Modern Painters*. Outlook Verlag GmBH (Germany), 2018.

Russell, Roslyn. *The Business of Nature: John Gould and Australia*. National Library of Australia, 2011.

Ruurs, Rob. "Review – Carel Fabritius: Complete Edition, by Christopher Brown." *Simiolus: Netherlands Quarterly for the History of Art* 12, no. 4 (1981): 263–265.

Schnier, J. "The Symbolic Bird in Medieval and Renaissance Art." *American Imago* 9, no. 2 (1952): 89–126.

Silberman, Robert. "Why a Duck? Birds in Art and Bird Art." *Smithsonian Studies in American Art* 3, no. 2 (Spring 1989): 63–79.

Spear, Jeffrey. "Gods and Dancing Girls: A Letter from 1802 Madras." *The Wordsworth Circle* 31, no. 3 (Summer 2000): 142–149.

Sutton, G. "Ornithological Literature." *The Wilson Bulletin* 79, no. 2 (1967): 249–251.

The Telegraph. "Keith Shackleton, Artist – Obituary." The Telegraph (internet; 24 April 2015). https://www.telegraph.co.uk/news/obituaries/11561502/Keith-Shackleton-artist-obituary.html

Tree, Isabella. *The Bird Man: the Extraordinary Story of the Victorian Ornithologist John Gould*. London: Ebury Press, 2004.

Turner, Percy Moore. "Two Attributions to Carel Fabritius." *The Burlington Magazine* 38, no. 218 (May 1921): 220–229.

Walthew, Bob. *Eric Ennion: A Personal View*. Bury Press, 1983.

Weidensaul, Scott. *Of a Feather: a Brief History of American Birding*. Orlando, FL: Harvest Books, 2007.

Wetmore, Frank Alexander. "Biographical Memoir of Robert Ridgway, 1850–1929." *Biographical Memoirs: National Academy of Sciences of the United States of America* 15 (1931): 57–101.

Wheye, Darryl, Donald Kennedy, and Paul R. Ehrlich. *Humans, Nature, and Birds: Science Art from Cave Walls to Computer Screens*. New Haven, CT: Yale University Press, 2008.

White, C. "Review of Birds of South Africa." *Journal of Field Ornithology* 53, no. 3 (1982): 296–297.

Whitley, Gilbert P. "The Life and Work of Tom Iredale (1880–1972)." *Australian Zoologist* 17, no. 2 (1972): 65–125.

Wikipedia. Jakob Bogdani (internet; 21 July 2018). https://en.wikipedia.org/wiki/Jakob_Bogdani

Wikipedia. Book of Nature (internet; 20 Sept 2018). https://en.wikipedia.org/wiki/Book_of_Nature

Wikipedia. Ray Harm (internet; 9 Jun 2018). https://en.wikipedia.org/wiki/Ray_Harm

Wikipedia. Melchior D'Hondecoeter (internet; 25 Jan. 2018). https://en.wikipedia.org/wiki/Melchior_d%27Hondecoeter

Wikipedia. John Gerrard Keulemans (internet; 4 Jun 2018). https://en.wikipedia.org/wiki/John_Gerrard_Keulemans

Wikipedia. Prideaux John Selby (internet; 2 July 2018). https://en.wikipedia.org/wiki/Prideaux_John_Selby

Wikisource. Woman of the Century/Graceanna Lewis (internet; 23 Dec 2017). https://en.wikisource.org/wiki/Woman_of_the_Century/Graceanna_Lewis

Williams, James. *Edward Lear*. Liverpool, UK: Liverpool University Press, 2018:13–42.

Wilson, David. "The Iconography of Mark Catesby." *Eighteenth-Century Studies* 4, no. 2 (1970): 169–183.

Winearls, Joan. "Allan Brooks, Naturalist and Artist (1869–1946)." *Scientia Canadensis: Canadian Journal of the History of Science, Technology and Medicine* 31, no. 1–2 (2008): 131–154.

Wood, Casey A. "Lady [Elizabeth] Gwillim – Artist and Ornithologist." *Ibis* 67, no. 3 (1925): 594–599.

"W. S." "Recent Literature: Cayley's Australian Finches in Bush and Aviary." *The Auk: Ornithological Advances* 50, no. 1 (Jan 1933): 132–133.

"W. S." "Recent Literature: Mathew's The Birds of Australia." *The Auk: Ornithological Advances* 44, no. 3 (Jul 1927): 435–442.

INDEX

CREDITS

Alamy: 39; /Artokoloro Quint Lox Limited 40-41, 79; /Asar Studios 35; /Chronicle 91; /History and Art Collection 131t; /Historic Images 10t; /Len Collection 127tl, 127l; /LLP Collection 76, 80; /Natural History Museum 62, 78, 144; /Painters 135t; / The Picture Art Collection 12, 64, 132; /Peter Horree 15; / Ariadne Van Zandbergen 6; /**Biodiversity Heritage Library:** 129; /**Bonhams:** 7; /**Bridgeman Images:** Larder with a Servant, c.1635-1640 (oil on panel), Snyders or Snijders, Frans (1579-1657) / Mead Art Museum, Amherst College, MA, USA / Museum purchase 8; /Pelicans, 1951 (silkscreen), Turner, Janet E. (1914-1988) / Dallas Museum of Art, Texas, USA / Dallas Art Association Purchase 11; / A Girl with a Parrot, Netscher, Caspar (1639-84) (after) / Snowshill Manor, Gloucestershire, UK / National Trust Photographic Library 16; / The Bird's Concert (oil on canvas), Snyders, Frans (1579-1657) (after) / Musee des Beaux-Arts, Dunkirk, France 20-21; / Two Iceland Falcons (oil on canvas), Bogdani or Bogdany, Jakob (1660-1724) / Nottingham City Museums and Galleries (Nottingham Castle) 28; /Coursing the Hare, illustration to Richard Blome's 'The Gentleman's Recreation' pub. 1686 (pen and ink with wash on paper), Barlow, Francis (1626-1702) / Leeds Museums and Galleries (Leeds Art Gallery) U.K. 31; / A Decoy, Barlow, Francis (1626-1702) / Clandon Park, Surrey, UK / National Trust Photographic Library 33; /An Owl being Mobbed by other Birds, Barlow, Francis (1626-1702) / Ham House, Surrey, UK / National Trust Photographic Library 34t; /Still Life with a Parrot, Fruit and Dead Birds / Ormesby Hall, North Yorkshire, UK / National Trust Photographic Library 36; /Fruit in a Pewter Bowl with a Parrot, Bogdani or Bogdany, Jakob (1660-1724) / Anglesey Abbey, Cambridgeshire, UK / National Trust Photographic Library 37; /Variety of Ducks by a Pool, Bogdani or Bogdany, Jakob (1660-1724) / Private Collection / Photo © Rafael Valls Gallery, London, UK 38t; / Cockerels and Pigeons, Bogdani or Bogdany, Jakob (1660-1724) / Private Collection / © Partridge Fine Arts, London, UK 38b; / A Turkey, Peacocks and Chickens in a Landscape, Cradock, Marmaduke (1660-1717) (attr. to) / Springhill, County Londonderry, Northern Ireland / National Trust Photographic Library 40; /A Peacock and other Birds in an Ornamental Landscape (oil on canvas), Cradock, Marmaduke (1660-1717) (attr. to) / Private Collection / Photo © Christie's Images 42; /A Fox tethered to a Kennel, terrorising a Cock, Hen and Chicks, Cradock, Marmaduke (1660-1717) / Middlethorpe Hall, North Yorkshire, UK / National Trust Photographic Library 43; / Watercolour illustration from a book of rare birds by G Edwards 1750. George Edwards (1694-1773) was a British naturalist and ornithologist. He travelled extensively through Europe, studying natural history and birds in particular. He gained some recognition for his coloured drawings, and published his first work in 1743-the first volume of A Natural History of Uncommon Birds. / Universal History Archive/UIG 44; / Haematopus palliatus / Natural History Museum, London, UK 46; /A Great White Crested Cockatoo (gouache on blue paper), Schouman, Aert (1710-92) / Fitzwilliam Museum, University of Cambridge, UK 47; /The ivory-billed woodpecker and willow oak (pen & ink with w/c on paper), Catesby, Mark (1679-1749) / Royal Collection Trust © Her Majesty Queen Elizabeth II, 2019 48; /Cyanocitta cristata / Natural History Museum, London, UK 51t; /Dogwood: Cornus florida, and Mocking Bird from the "Natural History of Carolina" (1730-48), Catesby, Mark (1679-1749) / Lindley Library, RHS, London, UK 51b; /Upupa epops / Natural History Museum, London, UK 52; / atercolour illustration from a book of rare birds by G Edwards 1750. George Edwards (1694-1773) was a British naturalist and ornithologist. He travelled extensively through Europe, studying natural history and birds in particular. He gained some recognition for his coloured drawings, and published his first work in 1743-the first volume of A Natural History of Uncommon Birds. / Universal History Archive/UIG 53, 54; / The Northern Penguin, 1749-73 (coloured engraving), Edwards, George (1694-1773) (after) / Private Collection / © Purix Verlag Volker Christen 55; /Dodo, Raphus cucullatus, extinct, and guinea pig, Cavia porcellus. Handcoloured copperplate engraving by Johann Sebastian Leitner after an

illustration by George Edwards in Johann Michael Seligmann's Collection of Various Foreign and Rare Birds, Jan Sepp, Amsterdam, 1772. / © Florilegius 56; / Lesser king bird of paradise, Cicinnurus regius. Illustration copied from George Edwards. Handcoloured copperplate engraving from "" The Naturalist's Pocket Magazine,"" Harrison, London, 1802. / © Florilegius 57; /Red-billed Toucan, 1748 (watercolour) , Schouman, Aert (1710-92) / Rijksmuseum, Amsterdam, The Netherlands 58; / Two red faced lovebirds and a waxbill, 1756 (chalk, w/c & pencil on paper), Schouman, Aert (1710-92) / Private Collection / Photo © Agnew's, London 59; / A Long-tailed Widowbird and a blue-crowned hanging parrot, 1783 (chalk, w/c & pencil on paper), Schouman, Aert (1710-92) / Private Collection / Photo © Agnew's, London 60; /Wild Fowl, Schouman, Aert (1710-92) / Private Collection / © Arthur Ackermann Ltd., London 61t; /BLACK WOODPECKER Wood engraving, c.1797, by Thomas Bewick. / Granger 66; / CROW Carrion Crow (Corvus corone). Wood engraving, c.1797, by Thomas Bewick. / Granger 67l; /PINTAIL DUCK Wood engraving, c.1804, by Thomas Bewick. / Granger 67r; /Great Ash-Coloured Shrike, illustration from 'The History of British Birds' by Thomas Bewick, first published 1797 (woodcut), Bewick, Thomas (1753-1828) / Private Collection 68; / HEN HARRIER Wood engraving, c.1797, by Thomas Bewick. / Granger 69; /Oceanites oceanicus, Wilson's storm petrel, Plate 270 from John James Audubon's Birds of America, original double elephant folio, 1827-30 (hand-coloured aquatint), Audubon, John James (1785-1851) / Natural History Museum, London, UK 81; / American Flamingo, from 'The Birds of America' (aquatint & engraving with hand-colouring), Audubon, John James (1785-1851) / Private Collection / Photo © Christie's Images 82; /Cacatua leadbeateri / Natural History Museum, London, UK 84; /Mocking Birds and Rattlesnake, from 'Birds of America', engraved by Robert Havell (1793-1878) (coloured engraving) (see 195126 for detail), Audubon, John James (1785-1851) (after) 86; /AUDUBON: PHOEBE Eastern Phoebe (Sayornis phoebe), from John James Audubon's 'The Birds of America,' 1827-1838. / Granger 87; /Great blue Heron, 1834 (coloured engraving), Audubon, John James (1785-1851) (after) / National Gallery of Art, Washington DC, USA 88; /AUDUBON: BALD EAGLE [Immature] Bald Eagle (Haliaeetus leucocephalus), from John James Audubon's 'Birds of America,' 1827-1838. / Granger 89; /Pelecanus erythrorynchos, American white pelican, Plate 311 from John James Audubon's Birds of America, original double elephant folio, 1827-30 (hand-coloured aquatint), Audubon, John James (1785-1851) / Natural History Museum, London, UK 90; /Great Bustard / Natural History Museum, London, UK 92; / Hen Harrier, Male and Female, Plate X from 'Illustrations of British Ornithology', 1819-34 (coloured etching), Selby, Prideaux John (1788-1867) / Edinburgh University Library, Scotland / With kind permission of the University of Edinburgh 93; /Eurasian Spoonbill / Natural History Museum, London, UK 94t; /Tyrannus savana / Natural History Museum, London, UK 94b; /Great Eared Owl, 1841 (hand-coloured engraving), Selby, Prideaux John (1788-1867) / Private Collection / Photo © Christie's Images 95; /Picus viridus / Natural History Museum, London, UK 96; / Himalayan Monal Pheasant, from 'A Century of Birds from the Himalaya Mountains', 1830-32, by John Gould (1804-41) (colour litho), Gould, Elizabeth (d.1841) / Natural History Museum, London, UK 97; /Trogon ardens / Natural History Museum, London, UK 98; /Ptiloris paradiseus / Natural History Museum, London, UK 100; /Geospiza magnirostris / Natural History Museum, London, UK 101; /Lorius chlorocercus / Natural History Museum, London, UK 102; /Ornithologie : representation d'un ara (Macrocercus Aracanga), gros perroquet a plumage colore. Planche tiree de ""The Family of Psittacidae, containing forty two lithographic plates, drawn from life"" par Edward Lear, 1832. The British Library Institution Reference: Shelfmark ID: 1899.f.21 'Macrocercus Aracanga', Macaw. 1832. Colourful macaw perched on a branch. Plate 7 from ""The Family of Psittacidae, containing forty two lithographic plates, drawn from life"" by Edward Lear. (London, 1832). ©The British Library Board/Leemage 105; / Crimson-Winged Parakeet (colour litho), Lear, Edward (1812-88) /Natural History Museum, London, UK 106; / "There was an old man with a beard, who said, 'It is just as I feared!'", from 'A Book of Nonsense', published by Frederick Warne and Co., London, c.1875 (colour litho), Lear, Edward (1812-88) / Private Collection / © Look and Learn 107; / Purple Heron (colour engraving), Lear, Edward (1812-88) / Private

Collection 108l; / Snowy Owl, 1832-1837 (hand-coloured lithograph), Lear, Edward (1812-88) / Private Collection / Photo © Christie's Images 108r; /Paloeornis Derbianus, 1831 (w/c on paper), Lear, Edward (1812-88) / The Right Hon. Earl of Derby 109; / Crimson bellied Tragopan, engraved by M. & N. Hanhart, 1870-72 (coloured engraving) by Wolf, Joseph (1820-99) & Smit, J. (fl.1870), Wolf, Joseph (1820-99) & Smit, J. (fl.1870) / Private Collection / Photo © Bonhams, London, UK 110; / Pavo muticus / Natural History Museum, London, UK 111b; /Shoebilled stork, 1861 (colour litho), Wolf, Joseph (1820-99) / Zoological Society of London 112t; / Chrysolophus amherstiae / Natural History Museum, London, UK 112b; / Argusianus argus grayi / Natural History Museum, London, UK 113; /Ceratagymna elata / Natural History Museum, London, UK 148; /A Water Turkey, Mexican Cormorant and a Mexican Grebe, 1934 (w/c & gouache on paper), Brooks, Allan (1869-1946) / National Geographic Image Collection 121; / Huia, from 'A History of the Birds of New Zealand' by Walter Lawry Buller, 1873 (hand-coloured litho), Keulemans, Johan Gerard (1842-1912) / Mark and Carolyn Blackburn Collection of Polynesian Art 122; /Bluebellied Roller, 1893 (hand-coloured lithograph), Keulemans, Johan Gerard (1842-1912) / Private Collection / Photo © Christie's Images 124; /Accipiter nisus / Natural History Museum, London, UK 128; /A Woodcock and Chicks, 1933 (pencil and watercolour heightened with white), Thorburn, Archibald (1860-1935) / Private Collection / Photo © Christie's Images 130b; /Carduelis carduelis / Natural History Museum, London, UK 131; /A Cat and a Chaffinch, 1885 (oil on canvas), Liljefors, Bruno Andreas (1860-1939) / National-museum, Stockholm, Sweden 134; /Black grouse mating game in the moss, 1907 (oil on canvas), Liljefors, Bruno Andreas (1860-1939) / Private Collection / Photo © O. Vaering 135b; /Various ibis perch lakeside, 1932 (colour litho), Brooks, Allan (1869-1946) / National Geographic Image Collection 136; /Strawberry finches, a Bengali finch and Java sparrows (colour litho), Brooks, Allan (1869-1946) / National Geographic Image Collection 138; /Two Swallow-tailed Kites, 1933 (colour litho), Brooks, Allan (1869-1946) / National Geographic Image Collection 139; /Passenger Pigeon, Eastern Morning Dove (colour litho), Fuertes, Louis Agassiz (1874-1927) / Private Collection 141; / A pair of gadwalls, or Anas strepera, 1915 (colour litho), Fuertes, Louis Agassiz (1874-1927) / National Geographic Image Collection 142; / A pair of black flycatchers, also known as Phainopepla, 1914 (colour litho), Fuertes, Louis Agassiz (1874-1927) / National Geographic Image Collection 143l; / James Flamingos in the Andes (gouache, coloured pencil and pencil on board), Peterson, Roger Tory (1908-96) / Private Collection / Photo © Christie's Images 147t; / Bycanistes brevis / Natural History Museum, London, UK 148; /Phoeniconaias minor / Natural History Museum, London, UK 149; /Anastomus lamelligerus / Natural History Museum, London, UK 151; / Egrets (oil on canvas laid down on masonite), Botke, Jessie Arms (1883-1971) / Private Collection / Photo © Christie's Images 160; / White Peacock and Solphus Crested Cockatoos (oil on masonite), Botke, Jessie Arms (1883-1971) / Private Collection / Photo © Christie's Images 161; /Manchurian Cranes (oil & gold leaf on masonite), Botke, Jessie Arms (1883-1971) / Private Collection / Photo © Christie's Images 162; /Sacred Cranes in Tropical River (oil on masonite), Botke, Jessie Arms (1883-1971) / Private Collection / Photo © Christie's Images 163l; /White Peacocks and Magnolia (oil & gold leaf on canvas), Botke, Jessie Arms (1883-1971) / Private Collection / Photo © Christie's Images 163r; /Birds, illustration from 'Life in Pond and Stream', 1943 (colour litho), Ennion, Eric (1900-81) / Private Collection 164; /Bearded Tits, illustration from The Sphere, 1953 (colour litho), Ennion, Eric (1900-81) / Private Collection 165; / Winter flock on flooded fields, illustration from 'The Lapwing', 1949 (colour litho), Ennion, Eric (1900-81) / Private Collection 166; / Ducks, illustration from 'Life in Pond and Stream', 1943 (colour litho), Ennion, Eric (1900-81) / Private Collection 167; / Penguins, Emperor and Others (gouache, watercolour and pencil on board), Peterson, Roger Tory (1908-96) / Private Collection / Photo © Christie's Images 16; / Two Ducks (gouache, watercolour and pencil on board), Peterson, Roger Tory (1908-96) / Private Collection / Photo © Christie's Images 169l; /Warbler (gouache, watercolour and pencil on paper), Peterson, Roger Tory (1908-96) / Private Collection / Photo © Christie's Images 169r; / Woodpeckers (watercolour, gouache and pencil on paper), Peterson, Roger Tory (1908-96) / Private Collection / Photo © Christie's Images 171; /Oropendolas (gouache, watercolour and pencil on paper-board), Peterson, Roger Tory (1908-96) / Private Collection / Photo © Christie's Images 171l; / Tanagers (gouache, watercolour, pencil and ink on paperboard), Peterson, Roger Tory (1908-96) / Private Collection / Photo © Christie's Images 171r; /Guinea Fowl, 1951 (linocut), Turner, Janet E. (1914-1988) / Dallas Museum of Art, Texas, USA / Dallas Art Association Purchase 172; /At the Nest of the Heron, 1953 (silkscreen), Turner, Janet E. (1914-1988) / Dallas Museum of Art, Texas, USA

/ Gift of the Artist 176; /Chickens, c.1948 (linocut), Turner, Janet E. (1914-1988) / Dallas Museum of Art, Texas, USA /Carcass Caucus, 1971 (colour embossed linocut & screenprint), Turner, Janet E. (1914-1988) / National Academy of Design, New York, USA 177; /Richard H. McLarry Prize, 2nd Southwestern Exhibition of Prints and Drawings, 1949 178b; /Beginning of Night, 1962 (linoleum cut & silkscreen), Turner, Janet E. (1914-1988) / Dallas Museum of Art, Texas, USA / gift of the Dallas Print and Drawing Society 179; /Goldeneye female with young, illustration from 'Wildfowl of Europe', 1972 (colour litho), Burn, Hilary (b.1946) / Private Collection 202; /Wigeon with young, illustration from 'Wildfowl of Europe', 1972 (colour litho), Burn, Hilary (b.1946) / Private Collection 203t; /Mandarin Ducks with young, illustration from 'Wildfowl of Europe', 1972 (colour litho), Burn, Hilary (b.1946) 203b; /Eider Duck, male and female with ducklings, illustration from 'Wild-fowl of Europe', 1972 (colour litho), Burn, Hilary (b.1946) / Private Collection 204; / Canada Geese, illustration from 'Wildfowl of Europe', 1972 (colour litho), Burn, Hilary (b.1946) / Private Collection 205; /© Elizabeth Butterworth: 196, 206-209; / Fondo Antiguo de la Biblioteca de la Universidad de Sevilla: 49; /Google Art Project: 14; /Google Cultural Institute: 18-19; /Jonathan Grant Galleries Ltd & ARTIS Gallery/© Ray Ching: 200-201; /© Lars Jonsson: 199, 210-213; /Estate of Fenwick Lansdowne: 192-195; /Michigan State University: 32; /Missouri Botanical Garden Library: 50; /Courtesy Manooka Pty Ltd: 188-191; /National Library of Australia: 147b, 152, 153t, 153b, 154, 155l, 155r; /Private Collection: 9, 17, 21, 23, 24. 25, 27, 34b, 65, 71-75, 85, 99, 111t, 114-117, 123, 125t, 125b, 133, 137, 140, 143r, 150tl, 150tr, 150b, 156-159; /Rijksmuseum: 61; /Photo © Muséum national d'Histoire naturelle, Dist. RMN-Grand Palais / image du MNHN, bibliothèque central: 10b; /Courtesy of Rountree Tryon Galleries: 184-187; / Scovil Galen Ghosh Literary Agency, Inc./© David Sibley 214-217; /The Estate of Arthur Singer: 175, 180-183; /© 2019. Photo Smithsonian American Art Museum/ Art Resource/Scala, Florence: Turner, Janet (1914-1988): Wintering Snow Geese, 1968. Color linoleum cut and screenprint, image: 14 3/4 x 35 in. (37.5 x 88.9 cm). Gift of the artist (1973.21.2). Washington DC, Smithsonian American Art Museum 178t; /Smithsonian Institution Archives: 120, 126c, 126tr, 126r

Every effort has been made to acknowledge correctly and contact the source and/or copyright holder of each picture and Carlton Publishing Group apologises for any unintentional errors or omissions, which will be corrected in future editions of this book.